LEADER OF THE SKIES

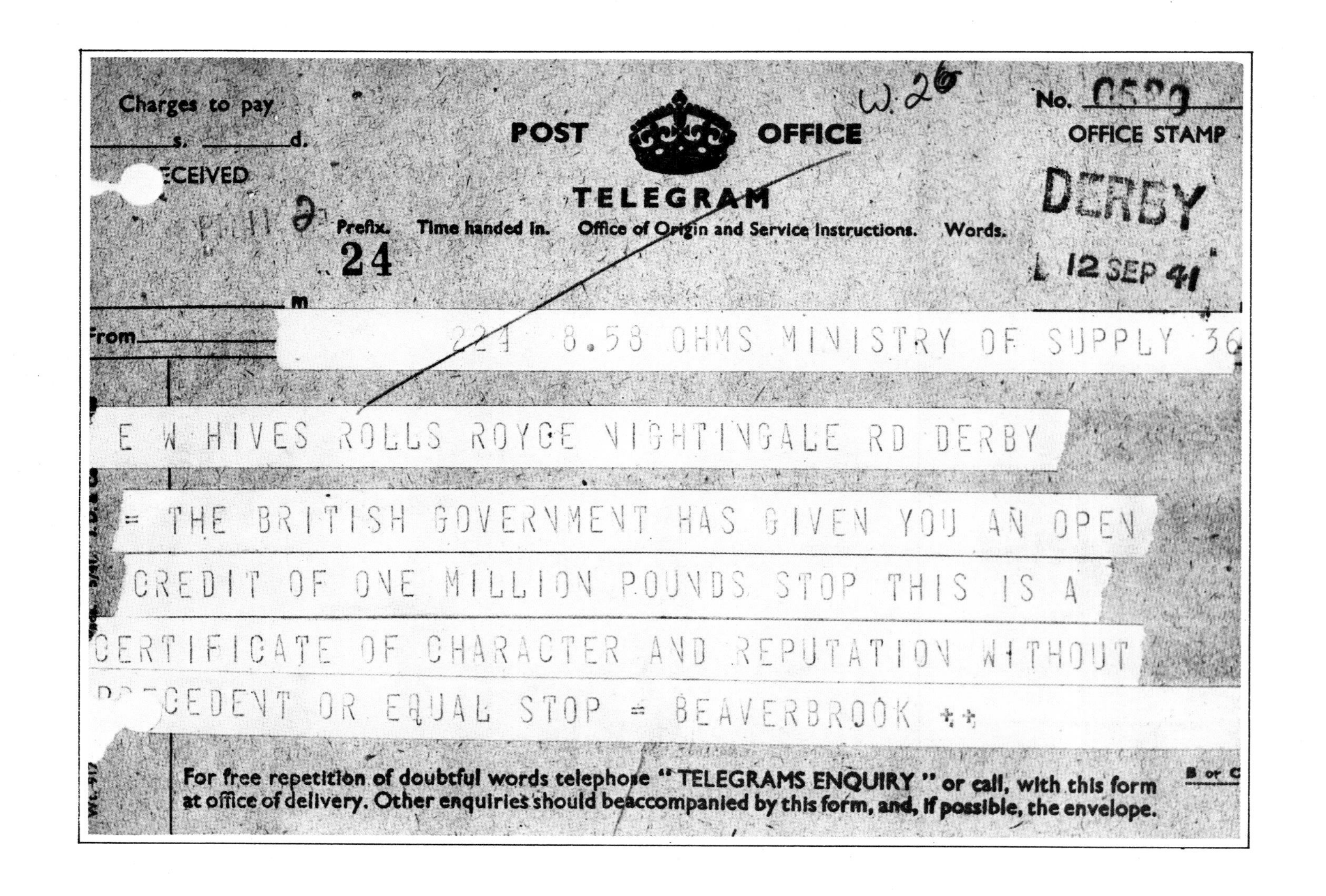

Charges to pay
s. d.
RECEIVED

POST OFFICE
TELEGRAM

No. 0582
OFFICE STAMP
DERBY
L 12 SEP 41

Prefix. Time handed in. Office of Origin and Service Instructions. Words.
24

From 224 8.58 OHMS MINISTRY OF SUPPLY 36

E W HIVES ROLLS ROYCE NIGHTINGALE RD DERBY

= THE BRITISH GOVERNMENT HAS GIVEN YOU AN OPEN CREDIT OF ONE MILLION POUNDS STOP THIS IS A CERTIFICATE OF CHARACTER AND REPUTATION WITHOUT PRECEDENT OR EQUAL STOP = BEAVERBROOK ++

For free repetition of doubtful words telephone "TELEGRAMS ENQUIRY" or call, with this form at office of delivery. Other enquiries should be accompanied by this form, and, if possible, the envelope.

B or C

LEADER OF THE SKIES

ROLLS-ROYCE: THE FIRST SEVENTY-FIVE YEARS

BY MICHAEL DONNE

FREDERICK MULLER LIMITED · LONDON

All illustrations in this book are from the Rolls-Royce archives with the exception of the following:

Arthur Gibson - back cover (Hawks of the RAF Red Arrows).
Boeing - 66 (top photo), 104 (bottom photo), 151 (bottom photo), 154.
British Aerospace - 63 (all photos), 77 (both photos), 106 (bottom photo), 108, 114, 117, 118, 121 (both photos), 124.
British Airways - 62 (top photo), 64 (bottom photo), 107 (top photo), 109, 111.
British Hovercraft Corporation - 129, 130.
Fokker - 112.
Gulfstream American - 107 (bottom photo).
Lockheed - 88, 89, 106 (top photo) 155, 156 (both photos), 157 (bottom photo).
McDonnell Douglas - 119, 151 (top photo).
NASA - 157 (top photo).
Royal Air Force - 59, 66 (bottom photo), 80.
Royal Navy - 132, 136, 138 (both photos), 139, 140.
Short Brothers - 15, 29 (bottom photo), 30 (top photo), 45.
Westland - 125 (bottom photo), 126.

First published in Great Britain 1981 by Frederick Muller Limited, London NW2 6LE

The publishers gratefully acknowledge the assistance of Rolls-Royce Limited.

Donne, Michael
Leader of the skies.
1. Rolls-Royce - History
2. Aircraft engine industry - Great Britain - History
I. Title
338.7'62913435'0941 HD9711.G74R5

ISBN 0-584-10476-6

Edited by Catherine Cohen
Designed by Colin Lewis
Typeset by D.P. Press Ltd. Sevenoaks, and printed in Italy

CONTENTS

PREFACE

Vouchsafe to those that have not read the story,
That I may prompt them: and of such as have,
I humbly pray them to admit the excuse
Of time, of numbers and due course of things,
Which cannot in their huge and proper life
Be here presented.

Chorus, Act V, *Henry V*

Opposite: *Royce's first internal combustion engine – a ten-horsepower two-cylinder model on test in 1903 for one of the Royce prototype cars. This may truly be said to be the origin of the Rolls-Royce internal combustion engine. It may be seen that from the outset Royce believed in bench testing and development. The power of the engine was absorbed by a Royce dynamo.*

This book is not intended to be the definitive history of the first seventy-five years of Rolls-Royce. That has yet to be written. Rather, it is an encapsulation of the salient events of a turbulent and sometimes even traumatic three-quarters of a century, during which many thousands of skilled men and women dedicated their working lives to the service of Rolls-Royce, and through it to their country. This book is really theirs, for without them, Rolls-Royce could never have existed, let alone survived. If, for reasons of length, the text does them all less than justice, I hope the pictures will recompense by showing what resulted from their skills.

My personal thanks are due to many inside the company, too numerous to name, but particularly Nigel Rowe, Alan Brothers, Mike Evans, and Jim Cownie. Jack Titley and his team were responsible for many of the pictures. My thanks are also due to those who helped with the pictures at British Airways, British Aerospace, the RAF, and in companies such as Short Brothers, Westland, Boeing, Lockheed, and in many airlines world-wide.

Then there are those charming ladies who typed the text so industriously – Gloria Costa, Sue Gee and Philippa King.

Finally, my thanks are due to my wife, who sat alone without complaint whilst I burned the midnight oil.

Michael Donne, London, 1981.

INTRODUCTION

THE DAWN OF FLYING

Opposite: The Honourable C.S. Rolls about to make a balloon ascent from the Monmouth gasworks. On the left of the balloon basket are his parents, Lord and Lady Llangattock. Immediately behind Lady Llangattock is Colonel Capper, Commandant of the Army Balloon School at Farnborough. To the right of the balloon, in a flat hat, moustached and with his left arm at his hip is T.O. Smith, Rolls' personal chaffeur and mechanic.

In the opening years of this century, flying as we understand it today was still just over mankind's horizon, tantalisingly beyond his grasp. Nonetheless, the early part of the first decade promised exciting technological possibilities in aeronautics, for much pioneering work had been done, and continued quietly on both sides of the Atlantic. The world was moving on from the era of the Victorians, whose own scientific, technical and engineering achievements in transport had been stupendous. The development of the railways, and of steamships had wrought tremendous changes. The motor car had made its appearance although it was still in a comparatively raw stage of development. But even with these achievements to their credit, some of the most illustrious scientists and engineers of the day remained sceptical of the possibility of men ever propelling themselves safely through the air.

Men had dreamed of flying for centuries, and had even made crude attempts in the Middle Ages, by jumping from towers with bird-like wings attached to their backs, or on their arms and legs, to almost certain injury or death. Eminent thinkers, like Leonardo da Vinci around 1500, had designed 'flapping wings', ornithopters and helicopters (some of his beautiful design drawings still exist) but neither he nor anyone else ever built a successful flying machine from his studies.

The nearest approach to practical aviation, exciting and dramatic in itself, was ballooning, or 'aerostation' as it was first called.

Ballooning effectively began with the French Montgolfier brothers in the latter part of the eighteenth century, and it quickly swept the Continent. It achieved a respectable aeronautical status in France as a means of military observation over the battlefield, and of carrying messages from beleagured towns, and subsequently it evolved through the nineteenth century into something of a sport for the adventurous well-to-do. The British government set up Her Majesty's Balloon Factory at Farnborough in 1894 (which

BROS
MAKERS
LONDON

was eventually to evolve into today's Royal Aircraft Establishment on the same location).

But even this interest in aviation through ballooning was still not enough to convince some of the most eminent men that manned, powered flight was on the way. The physicist Lord Kelvin, in a letter to Major B.F.S. Baden-Powell in December, 1896, rejecting an invitation to join the Aeronautical Society of Great Britain (set up in 1866), declared: "I have not the smallest molecule of faith in aerial navigation other than ballooning or of expectation of good results from any of the trials we hear of" - an attitude of mind not uncommon among his contemporaries.

But while there were those who derided the possibilities of manned, powered flight, there were many others who quietly believed in its inevitability, even though they did not know precisely how it was going to be achieved. Today, they are recognised as brilliant technical innovators, but in their day they were either ignored, ridiculed, or even sometimes villified.

The painstaking, methodical research of these men, who throughout the nineteenth century pressed ahead with their experiments, at their own financial expense and often also at risk of life and limb, progressively built up the body of knowledge that was to open the way for the practical aeronautical achievements of the early years of the twentieth century.

Sir George Cayley (1773-1857) is acknowledged as one of the greatest pioneers of aeronautics during the nineteenth century, although much of his work has only in recent years been given the credit it deserves. At his home at Brompton Hall, near Scarborough, he experimented with models of kites and gliders, and sent up several manned flights with gliders across a valley in which his coachman was successfully airborne. The coachman's feelings on the matter are not recorded.

Cayley was followed by many others, both in this country and on the Continent. By 1866, work had reached the point where several enthusiasts felt justified in giving a more scientific stimulus to aeronautical endeavour. Following the establishment of the Société Aerostatique et Météorologique de France in 1852, they formed the Aeronautical Society of Great Britain (later the Royal Aeronautical Society).

Among many men who figured prominently in aeronautical research in the later years of the nineteenth century were Lawrence Hargrave, an Australian who experimented with box-kites in the 1880s; Sir Hiram S. Maxim (1840-1916) who around the same time was experimenting with model wings and propellers, and built an unsuccessful steam-powered aircraft; Otto Lilienthal of Germany (1848-1896) who was one of the greatest pioneers of gliding flight, influencing many who came after including the Wright brothers; and Clément Ader of France (1841-1925) who attempted powered, manned 'hops' in a steam-driven model.

In the USA, Samuel Pierpont Langley (1834-1906), an astronomer, made steam-driven, unmanned models which flew distances of up to 4,200 feet (1280m). He was given United States government support to build a man-carrying aircraft, which he called an 'Aerodrome'. However it failed in tests on the Potomac River on 7th October and 8th December, 1903, and the venture was abandoned.

The proximity of those dates to the first successful powered, sustained and controlled flight in a heavier-than-air machine by the Wright brothers, Orville (1871-1948) and Wilbur (1867-1912), on 17th December, 1903, at Kill Devil Hill, near Kitty Hawk, on the North Carolina coast, was significant. For the bicycle-manufacturing Wrights, of Dayton, Ohio, who had begun their experiments in 1899 (although they had an interest in flying for nearly all their lives) were aware of Langley's work, but did not believe it was on the right track. As Wilbur later admitted, they preferred to follow Lilienthal's line of attack, as well as undertake their own experiments.

But even the success of the Wright brothers, vital as it eventually proved to be, did not immediately set the world alight. They kept much of their work secret, and continued to perfect their 'Flyer' in private, eventually achieving flights of thirty-eight minutes over distances of just over twenty-four miles (38·62kms) in October, 1905, by which time they felt that they had 'conquered the air'. But lack of government interest in their efforts in both America and Britain was a great disappointment, and they stayed out of the limelight for over two more years. It was not until 1908 that they began to demonstrate publicly their improved Flyer in both the USA and France.

It was as well that they did so then. Activity in France, in particular, had been building up rapidly, in the interim, following a visit to that country by Octave Chanute (1832-1910), another pioneering US aeronaut. Chanute knew much of what the Wrights had achieved and in his enthusiasm made little secret of it when he visited Europe. As a result, work by such pioneers as Gabriel and Charles Voisin, Louis Blériot and Alberto Santos-Dumont, a Brazilian, was greatly stimulated. The latter achieved the first officially accredited powered flight of 328 feet (100m) in Europe on 12th November, 1906, with an aircraft called '14-bis'. Henri Farman arrived on the scene in France in 1907, while in England names such as S.F. Cody, J.W. Dunne and A.V. Roe began to emerge, among others.

Frederick Henry Royce when he was an apprentice with the Great Northern Railway workshops at Peterborough.

The time was clearly ripe for the Wrights to re-emerge. By August, 1908, Wilbur Wright was in France, giving public demonstrations in his Flyer, first at Hunaudières Racecourse at Le Mans, and then at the nearby military Camp d'Auvours, while at the same time, Orville was giving public demonstrations at Fort Myer near Washington in the USA. By December, Wilbur had made over a hundred flights, logging a total of more than

twenty-six hours in the air. Powered flying had come to stay. And on 8th October, 1908, Wilbur took up as passengers from Camp d'Auvours, a number of people, including some well-known balloonists – Griffith Brewer, Frank Hedges Butler, Major Baden-Powell, and the Honourable Charles Stewart Rolls who was also a well-known motorist. It was their enthusiastic accounts of the flights that encouraged the Short brothers to start building aircraft instead of balloons.

It is against this background that the eventual evolution of Rolls-Royce itself has to be seen. In the early years of the century, many of the figures in British and world aeronautics who eventually became household names, had either not been heard of, or were only just emerging. These figures included Rolls and Royce, the Short brothers and Alliott Verdon Roe, in Britain. There was still much to do before the manned, powered aeroplane could become anything more than a rare object of wonder.

C.S. Rolls and Frederick Henry Royce themselves did not even suspect at the dawn of the century that within a few years each would be making his own individual contribution to the developing arts of flying and aero-engine manufacture. Neither they, nor any of the other pioneers, could envisage the extraordinary progress that the aeroplane was to make over the next seventy-five years, both as a military weapon and as a means of commercial transport, virtually changing the political, economic and sociological map of the world.

The technological development of the aeroplane over the past three-quarters of a century has been more rapid than almost any branch of technology, other than perhaps the nuclear sciences and electronics, which are in any event much younger. It took mankind over two thousand years to learn to fly, but having once done so, he has carried the aeroplane from a flimsy and precarious contraption of wood, canvas and wire, puttering along at a few miles an hour, to sleek high-speed arrow-heads of metal, such as Concorde, which can carry up to one hundred people at a time through the air, over distances of several thousand miles, at speeds of more than twice that of sound itself, whilst for military purposes even greater speeds and more devastating capabilities have already been achieved.

Millions of people world-wide now take it for granted that they can fly from almost anywhere in the world to anywhere else. The present generation accepts flying as a natural activity, as inevitable to their lives as many other of the technological miracles of the twentieth century, such as the radio and television. They can no more conceive of what life would be like in a world without aviation than their great-grandparents could conceive of the changes that the aeroplane would unleash. Even today, seventy-eight years after the Wright brothers' memorable flight at Kill Devil Hill, mankind has probably only glimpsed some of the possibilities that aviation is likely to make to everyday life, despite all the aeronautical developments that have occurred.

Opposite: *The Honourable C.S. Rolls with one of his Wright Flyers. Rolls was the first British private citizen to own an aeroplane.*

1 GENESIS (1906-1914)

Although Rolls-Royce was formally created on 15th March, 1906, the story of the company effectively begins nearly two years earlier, when in May, 1904, two remarkable men of disparate births, upbringing and character met for the first time in Manchester. They took an instant liking to each other, and established a partnership that was to endure in name until the present day, although one of them was to meet a tragic early death only six years after their meeting.

The Honourable Charles Stewart Rolls, the third son of the first Lord Llangattock, was born in 1877. He was a fearless and adventurous child, and these qualities were to mark everything he did in his comparatively short life. Tall, slim, handsome, patrician in manner, but regarded as parsimonious by his friends, his father's wealth and his social position enabled him to indulge his tastes to such effect that he was to become a balloonist and pioneer motorist and aviator, achieving great proficiency in all three fields. Educated at Eton and Trinity College, Cambridge, he was captain of the university racing cycling team, and he became the first person in Cambridge to own a motor-car.

Academically brilliant, he took his MA, specialising in practical electricity, engineering, mechanics and applied sciences. Ballooning was one of his earliest passions, and in all he made over one hundred and thirty ascents. It was after a balloon flight from the Crystal Palace in September, 1901, that Rolls, together with Frank Hedges Butler, the latter's daughter Vera, and the balloon pilot, Stanley Spencer, set up the Aero Club, on 29th October, 1901 (it was eventually to become the Royal Aero Club on 15th February, 1910).

Rolls became an avid motor-racing enthusiast, entering many competitions at home and abroad, with considerable success, and he was a founder-member of the Automobile Club (later the Royal Automobile Club). One of Rolls' friends, Claude Johnson, was also a founder-member of the RAC, and was its first secretary, a

A line-up of famous pioneers of motor racing and aeronautics at Mussel Manor (the Aero Club's first flying ground in the Isle of Sheppey) on 4th May, 1909.

Standing, *left to right:* J.D.F. Andrews; Oswald Short; Horace Short; Eustace Short; Frank (later Sir Francis) McLean, the astronomer and aviator; Griffith Brewer (the Wrights agent in the British Empire); Frank Hedges Butler, Dr W.J.S. Lockyer, an astronomer, balloonist and pioneer of aerial photography; and Warwick Wright, a motor-racing pioneer. Seated, *left to right:* J.T.C. Moore-Brabazon (later Lord Brabazon of Tara); Wilbur Wright, Orville Wright, and the Hon. C.S. Rolls.

function he discharged with energy and enthusiasm. It was Rolls' interest in motor-cars, especially French vehicles, which became his paramount concern. He began to sell them through his own London-based company, C.S. Rolls and Company, first in Lillie Hall in Fulham and then in Conduit Street (where Rolls-Royce had its own London headquarters for many years, and which is still used by the now separate company, Rolls-Royce Motors). Claude Johnson was also a director of C.S. Rolls and Company, and was eventually to play a long and crucial role in the Rolls-Royce saga.

Rolls' adventurous and restless spirit was not totally satisfied with motoring, however, and in the first decade of this century he showed a strengthening interest in aviation. He had met the Wright brothers, Orville and Wilbur, in America in 1906, and had admired their endeavours. Following their first successful flight, Rolls' enthusiasm for aviation grew. Late in 1909 he was teaching himself to fly on a Wright Flyer at the Aero Club's new airfield at Mussel Manor, Shellbeach, in the Isle of Sheppey. On 8th March, 1910, he became the possessor of the (now Royal) Aero Club's Pilots' Certificate No. 2. His friend and former employee J.T.C. Moore-Brabazon, later Lord Brabazon of Tara, also a life-long

Frederick Henry Royce in 1907. This picture was taken for publicity purposes, following the successful completion of 15,000 miles non-stop in the original Silver Ghost. Not without a fuss, for Royce thought it a waste of time to stop work to have his photograph taken.

Ernest A. Claremont photographed circa 1907. Claremont and Royce were the co-founders of F.H. Royce and Co. in 1884. Together they built up the business in electrical and mechanical engineering at Cooke Street. Claremont was the first chairman of Rolls-Royce Limited.

motoring and aviation enthusiast, gained Certificate No. 1 the same day.

Rolls was the first British private citizen to buy an aeroplane. He bought two Wright Flyers built in England by the three Short brothers, Horace, Eustace and Oswald. The Shorts were also destined to become famous as the first manufacturers of aircraft in the world, at first building balloons at Battersea and then setting up their aircraft factory at Leysdown in the Isle of Sheppey, near Mussel Manor. Rolls also bought a French-built Astra Wright Flyer. During the first half of 1910, he took part in many aviation meetings and adventures, in the UK and on the Continent, including making the first double crossing of the English Channel between Dover and Sangatte without landing, in one day, on 2nd June, 1910, the year after Blériot had made the first crossing in a heavier-than-air craft from France to England. For his feat, Rolls was awarded the Royal Aero Club's gold medal.

However, long before his passion for aviation had become so consuming, and whilst still essentially a motoring salesman and enthusiast, Rolls had been introduced to Frederick Henry Royce.

Royce came from a totally different background – one of poverty, hardship, insufficient food, and an early introduction to hard work. There are even accounts of him sometimes being obliged to sustain himself solely on bread dipped in milk. He was born at Alwalton, near Peterborough in Lincolnshire, on 27th March, 1863, the fifth child of Mary and James Royce. James Royce was a miller whose business failed whilst his children were still very young. The family moved south in 1867, but his father died when Frederick Royce was still only nine. Forced by circumstances to help the rest of his family survive,

"Fred" Royce, as he was called, became first a newspaper boy with W.H. Smith & Son, and then a telegraph messenger boy at the Mayfair Post Office.

However, an aunt was able to find enough money, £20 a year, to apprentice Royce to the Peterborough works of the Great Northern Railway. There, he was happy for perhaps the first time in his life. He lived with a skilled fitter, Mr Yarrow, whose own son was apprenticed to the railway. In the evenings which Royce could spare from educating himself at the evening institute, Mr Yarrow taught him much of his own skills of tool-making and handling in his back-garden workshop.

But, after three years, in 1879, the aunt's money ran out, the apprenticeship had to end, and Royce, now sixteen, was on the streets again. He moved north, and found a job with a tool-making firm in Leeds where he earned eleven shillings for a fifty-four hour week. It was around this time that he also became interested in electricity, and he returned to London and found a job as an electrical tester with the Electric Light and Power Company.

Royce was good at the job, and he was also continuing to educate himself at the Finsbury Polytechnic. He was promoted and sent back north to Liverpool, as an engineer with the Lancashire Maxim and Western Electric Company, a subsidiary of the London company. But the London company and the subsidiary failed, and Royce was out of a job again.

By this time, however, Royce had met Ernest A. Claremont, another young man who shared his enthusiasm for electrical engineering and hard work. Claremont eventually played a major role in the Rolls-Royce story. Royce and Claremont became close friends and associates. In 1893 they married two sisters, the daughters of Alfred Punt, a London businessman.

In 1884 Royce and Claremont decided to pool their slender resources. Royce had £20, Claremont about £50. They founded a firm called F.H. Royce and Company, in Cooke Street, Manchester, where they made and sold electrical equipment, and lived above their workshop. Royce invented an electric household bell-set which was an instant success, setting the little company on the road to better days. Then he invented a new dynamo, which was also highly successful. As a result of the company's growth it was restructured in 1894, to become Royce Limited, still specialising in electrical equipment, but now also including another Royce invention, electric cranes which were very reliable, and sold well. Some are still in service today.

It was in the early years of this century, with better times, more cash, a wife and a house in Knutsford, that Royce, who was now forty, became interested in motor-cars. One of his first acquisitions was a 1902 second-hand 10hp French Decauville, to enable him to commute between his home and his Cooke Street factory. At that time, he had no intention of designing and building cars. But his inventive mind would not allow him merely to drive it. He took it apart to see if he could improve it, and in the process concluded that not only could he design a better vehicle, but also that he ought to do so.

Thus, the first Royce car, a 10hp, two-cylinder, four-seater, was begun late in 1903 with the aid of two apprentices, Eric Platford and Tom S. Haldenby (both of whom stayed with Rolls-Royce, attaining very senior positions in the company). The car emerged from the Cooke Street factory on 1st April, 1904. On an immediate road test from Cooke Street to Knutsford, it was

AX148
A3

judged impeccable – nothing fell off, and it was smooth and quiet. But Royce himself was not satisfied, and continued to improve it. Only three of those original 10hp cars were built – and one was still being used in the company's Derby works in the 1920s, carrying mail.

Henry Edmunds, a shareholder in Royce Limited, was also a dedicated motorist and a friend of Rolls. He was deeply impressed by Royce's efforts and decided to bring Rolls and Royce together – despite Ernest Claremont's growing concern at what he regarded as Royce's neglect of the electrical business in his new-found enthusiasm for cars. Edmunds knew that Rolls was looking for a partner. Rolls had earlier confided to him that it was his ambition to have: "A motor-car connected with his name so that in the future it might be a household word, just as much as 'Broadwood' or 'Steinway' in connection with pianos, or 'Chubbs' in connection with safes".

That Manchester meeting in early May, 1904, was an immediate success. Edmunds wrote long afterwards that they all went to lunch at the Midland Hotel at Manchester. "I think both men took to each other at first sight," he said. "They eagerly discussed the prospects and requirements of the automobile industry which was still in its early infancy. Mr Rolls then went to see for himself the Royce car . . ."

Rolls liked the car, had it delivered to London, and got Claude Johnson out of bed to drive around in it with him. Thereafter, Rolls and Royce came to an agreement in 1904, following long negotiations, whereby Royce Limited would manufacture cars of 10, 15, 20 and 30hp, and C.S. Rolls and Company would sell them, under the joint name of Rolls-Royce, through a new distributing agency which was to be called Rolls-Royce Distributing Limited.

A view of one of the machine shops at the Cooke Street factory, Manchester. In the centre foreground of the picture is Jimmy Broom who, along with many others, came to Derby when Rolls-Royce moved. Although at one stage promoted to foreman in Derby, Jimmy returned to the shop floor as he felt happier working a machine.

Royce designed two other cars in 1905 and 1906. There was the Legalimit, to meet a passing fad for a town car that would not exceed the legal 20mph speed limit and the Landaulette par Excellence which competed with the electric brougham of the day. Neither car was a commercial success, and they were quickly abandoned. However, they taught Royce much about engine design, and many of their features were later to be incorporated into the design for the 40/50 horsepower Silver Ghost of 1906.

The agreement between Rolls and Royce worked well. The 10, 15, 20 and 30hp cars were a

Opposite: *A two-cylinder ten-horsepower Rolls-Royce at Duxford, September 1979.*

A 40/50hp chassis at the Derby works. The picture was taken about 1910. This chassis made its first appearance at the end of 1906. The thirteenth 40/50 chassis produced was used by the company as a demonstration car. It was given the name Silver Ghost.

Rolls-Royce built the chassis to customers' orders, the coachwork being built by a specialist coach-building company of the customer's choice. It was not until car production was resumed after the Second World War that Rolls-Royce manufactured complete motor cars. Even then a chassis could be purchased and coachwork chosen from another company.

great success with Rolls himself winning many national and international competitions with them, and firmly establishing the cars in the public mind at a time of fierce competition in the burgeoning motor trade. The partnership was so successful that it was cemented into a company, Rolls-Royce Limited, registered as a public company with an initial capital of £60,000 on 15th March, 1906. Royce put into it the motor-car side of Royce Limited, but the latter company continued as a separate entity in the electrical equipment business for many years until it was finally wound up after Royce's death in 1933. The first chairman of Rolls-Royce Limited was Ernest Claremont, Royce's old friend and partner, and Claude Johnson was also on the board along with Rolls and Royce. The secretary was John de Looze, who had joined Royce in 1894, and was a financial expert who served the company for many years. Later, in November, 1906, the capital of the company was raised to £200,000, with £100,000 of the shares being offered to the public, and both C.S. Rolls & Company and Rolls-Royce Distributing, were taken into Rolls-Royce Limited.

It was a happy relationship. Rolls, with his experience of public taste, gently guided Royce's inventive genius and engineering flair along lines designed to ensure that Rolls-Royce cars stayed ahead. However, Claude Johnson saw the need to specialise, and the range was sharply cut back to just one vehicle – a six-cylinder 40/50 horsepower model which appeared at the end of 1906. Royce thought it was the best car he had ever designed. An early example was named the Silver Ghost, and it completed a non-stop 15,000 miles (24,140kms) trial in excellent condition. It was hailed by the press, and it was effectively the vehicle that gave the company the soubriquet of building, "The Best Car In The World", a reputation which has remained with Rolls-Royce cars ever since. The Silver Ghost itself was to remain in production for nineteen years.

By 1907, it was clear that the Cooke Street, Manchester premises were no longer adequate for both expanding motor-car and electrical equipment production, and after a long search, a new site on which to build a factory for Rolls-Royce itself was found in Nightingale Road, Derby. The site was described at the time as having approaches, "very good and exceptionally level", while the town, albeit industrial, with the

The Honourable C.S. Rolls negotiating a corner in the Tourist Trophy race of 1906 on the Isle of Man. Two of the new 20hp four-cylinder models had been entered in the first ever TT race in 1905. Whilst Rolls was forced to retire by a gearbox problem, Percy Northey of Rolls-Royce, driving the other car, finished second. Riding as mechanic to Rolls is Eric Platford. Together with Tommy Haldenby he had been responsible for the testing of the prototype Royce engine. He was later to be the chief Rolls-Royce service engineer in Newfoundland supporting the first direct transatlantic flight attempts. In his last years with the company he was in charge of all production testing.

Midland Railway Company's works at hand, was nonetheless "exceptionally clean" and "comparatively free from smoke". Royce himself designed the machine shops, and the company began to transfer in 1907. The new premises were formally opened on 9th July, 1908.

Other changes lay ahead. Rolls was still restless. He continued to sell cars, but was very keen to concentrate more on aviation. He left the Rolls-Royce board in early 1910, amicably and at his own request, whilst remaining a shareholder, and began to fly more frequently. At a three-day flying meeting in Bournemouth, on 12th July,

A two-cylinder ten-horsepower Royce prototype. This was one of the pictures taken to persuade Rolls to journey to Manchester to meet Royce in 1904.

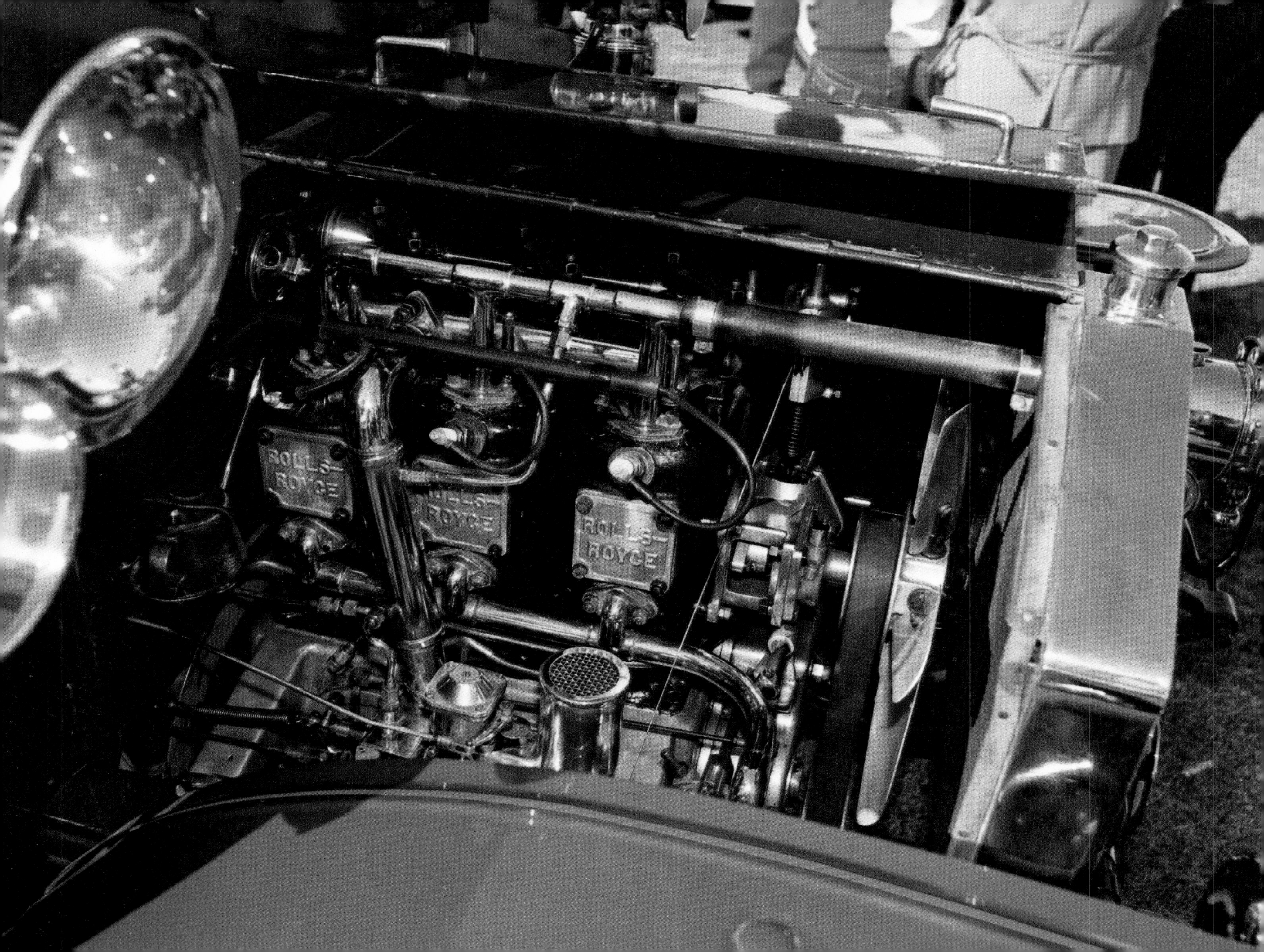
ROLLS-ROYCE
ROLLS-ROYCE
ROLLS-ROYCE

Charles Rolls driving the Wright brothers when they came to England in 1909. From left to right: Horace Short; Rolls; Orville Wright; Griffith Brewer, an agent for the Wrights and balloonist friend of Rolls; Wilbur Wright.

1910, he was killed instantly when his French-built Astra Flyer crashed on diving too steeply while he was trying to win a precision landing competition. He was only thirty-three, and yet he had achieved so much. Everyone was stunned, for Rolls had been very much a national and international figure.

However, the company Rolls had helped to found was by now sufficiently well established for it to survive. Royce not only had Claremont and de Looze to help him on financial affairs, there was also Claude Johnson, who had shown remarkable flair for publicity and marketing in the early days of the partnership. Johnson demonstrated his ability as a highly competent manager. It was Johnson who was to direct the company's day-to-day affairs as chief executive for many years to come, well into the 1920s. Particularly important was the way he guided the company through a crisis in 1911 when Royce, then middle-aged, fell gravely ill, largely as a result of overwork compounded by the shock of Rolls' death and his own early dietary deficiencies.

Royce recovered, but thereafter, his health was never good. He was obliged, apart from the war years, to spend his winters at Le Canadel, in the South of France – a spot where Johnson himself had a villa, and where Royce had gone for convalescence. Royce was enchanted with the place and there he built a house, the Villa Mimosa, along with an office (Le Bureau) and a residence for staff (Le Rossignol). He worked there each winter, concentrating on the design

Opposite: *The engine of the only known surviving three-cylinder 15-horsepower Rolls-Royce, taken at Duxford in 1979.*

The crash which killed Rolls, Bournemouth, 1910. Royce had modified the aircraft himself, only two days earlier.

activities of the company, leaving Claremont and Johnson to run the rest of the Rolls-Royce affairs. Royce returned only in the summers, first to St Margaret's Bay in Kent, and then to Elmstead, at West Wittering in Sussex. Royce was a good production engineer but he tended to disrupt the smooth flow of production whenever he spotted a design fault. His living arrangements ensured that he had the time and peace to concentrate upon design, whilst keeping well away from the day-to-day production affairs of the company which Claude Johnson had already demonstrated he could handle so well. This did not stop Royce, however, from bombarding those at Derby with endless notes and advice.

Rolls-Royce Limited continued to specialise in motor cars after Rolls' death. Royce had shown little interest in aviation, and the board had earlier rejected a suggestion by Rolls himself that the company should take a licence to build the Wright aeroplane – a factor which may have hastened Rolls' decision to leave the board in 1910. Royce did not believe there was a commercial future for such a venture.

However, the Silver Ghost went from success to success, and swept the board in the Alpine Rally of 1913. The team included as a test driver a young man called Ernest Hives, who had worked first with Rolls and then with Royce. The car won again in 1914.

The company was substantial, prosperous, and already famous. It might have remained a motor-car manufacturer for ever, had not the First World War erupted in August, 1914.

Opposite: *Rolls-Royce motor cars line up in Nightingale Road, Derby, on 9th July 1908 for the opening of the new works of Rolls-Royce Limited.*

The motor car nearest the camera is Silver Rogue, which was specially built for the 1908 Scottish Reliability Trials. Only three of these were made. They were known as "Type 70s" as they gave some 70hp compared with the normal 48. To achieve the extra power the engine was redesigned to incorporate overhead valves in place of the normal side valve layout.

2 WORLD WAR ONE

A Rolls-Royce 40/50hp armoured car in the desert. It was the Royal Naval Air Service that decided to use the chassis for armoured cars initially and their success was followed by orders from the War Office.

The outbreak of war in 1914 was critical for Rolls-Royce. Apart from Rolls' death and Royce's severe illness, it brought the first real crisis to the company. This resulted in the cancellation of all its orders for luxury motor cars and considerable uncertainty about immediate future activities.

This situation was soon resolved, when the company began to build 40/50hp chassis for army staff cars and ambulances. The same chassis was converted into an armoured car, which carried some 2¾ tons (2·8 tonnes) of armour-plate and armament. Some of these cars were used by Lawrence of Arabia, and some were even still to be found in service with the British armed forces at the start of the Second World War.

Clearly this activity was not likely to keep the company fully employed throughout what might well prove to be a long war, and the management looked around for other outlets for Rolls-Royce.

At the outbreak of war, aviation in Britain, and especially military aviation, was still very much in its infancy. The government had set up the Royal Aircraft (formerly Balloon) Factory at Farnborough, but there was no clear idea as to how to use the aeroplane as a weapon of war, or even how to go about developing it in a logical manner. Although much had already been achieved, such British aeroplanes and aero-

Colonel T.E. Lawrence wearing Arab dress is the passenger in this Silver Ghost in Damascus during World War I.

engines as existed at all in 1914 were either still in their early development stages, or were ultimately to prove unsuitable for combat purposes.

The most suitable aero-engines at that time were not British but French. As a result of an arrangement whereby major engineering companies were associated with specific government departments for war-work purposes, Rolls-Royce at that time was working closely with the Admiralty, and the latter suggested that the company should undertake the manufacture of aero-engines, notably those of Renault. Almost desperate for work, the company agreed, but Royce himself did not think highly of the Renault engine, and set out within days of the outbreak of war to design his first aero-engine.

Many different reasons for this decision have been given subsequently. One is that he genuinely felt that he could do a better job than anyone else. Another is that he was convinced at last that avaiation had come to stay, and that it represented an engineering challenge in its own right that his inventive brain could not ignore. Another is that he felt that he owed it to Rolls' memory to do something for the war effort. Yet another is that the Admiralty was anxious for him to do so, and encouraged him strongly. There is probably something in all of these reasons.

It was one of those pivotal decisions that was to influence the company's entire future. After studying existing engine designs, both British and Continental (one report suggests that he paid particular attention to Mercedes), Royce demonstrated once again his astonishing capacity for sustained intense concentration. He began work in August, 1914, on a twelve-cylinder water-cooled engine, in which the cylinders were arranged in two banks of six at a V-angle of sixty degrees, effectively becoming the prototype of a

Admiralty Airship 24 powered by Rolls-Royce Eagle engines. The Admiralty made use of airships for patrol work during the war. A series were built and considerable effort was devoted to this programme by a number of manufacturers, although with varying degrees of success. A section of the Rolls-Royce works in Derby was set up as the Royal Airship Drawing Office.

The Eagle Mk VIII on test at Derby. Royce had decided upon a liquid cooled engine of 12 cylinders, capable of delivering 200hp. Its crankcase, crankshaft, gears and connecting rods owed much to the design of the 40/50hp motor car engine but the cylinders and valve gear were to a degree similar to the latest Mercedes aero-engine practice. Each cylinder was forged separately and provided with a welded sheet metal water jacket. Each bank of cylinders carried a camshaft which operated overhead inlet and exhaust valves.

design pattern that was to be found in many subsequent Rolls-Royce piston engines.

The engine was running at 225hp on the testbed at Derby by February, 1915, by which time a small order for twenty-five engines had been granted by the Admiralty. Deliveries began later that year – an astonishing achievement of design, development and production.

The engine was called the Eagle, and thus began the company's habit of naming all its piston engines after birds of prey. Throughout the war, the Eagle was to be ordered in substantial numbers. It was to be steadily improved and produced in many versions, and to be used in many military, and eventually also civil, aeroplanes through into the 1930s, reflecting the inbuilt excellence of its basic design.

Royce did not stop there. His engineering flair and drive for perfection led to the development of three other aero-engines in the ensuing years of the war. The 75hp six-cylinder Hawk was in essence a derivative of the Eagle. Although originally intended for trainer aircraft, it was largely used as the power unit for small, non-rigid naval sea-patrol airships called Blimps. Nearly 60,000 hours were flown by British airships during the war, 36,000 of which were with Hawk engines, which achieved an exceptionally high degree of reliability. The Hawk also powered some BE-2E and Avro 504F aircraft.

The Eagle, however, was considered too heavy for the contemporary fighters that were beginning to emerge. The smaller 200hp Falcon, which was in essence, a scaled-down version of the Eagle, was developed in April, 1916. This, in the Series III version, was to become the engine of the famous "Brisfit" F2B Bristol Fighter (which remained in service with the Royal Flying Corps and later the Royal Air Force for ten years after

Porte Felixstowe Fury, powered by five Rolls-Royce Eagle VIIIs. Designed by Commander John Porte and built at Felixstowe Air Marine Experimental Station, this flying boat was making its maiden flight when the maroons were fired to announce the Armistice in 1918.

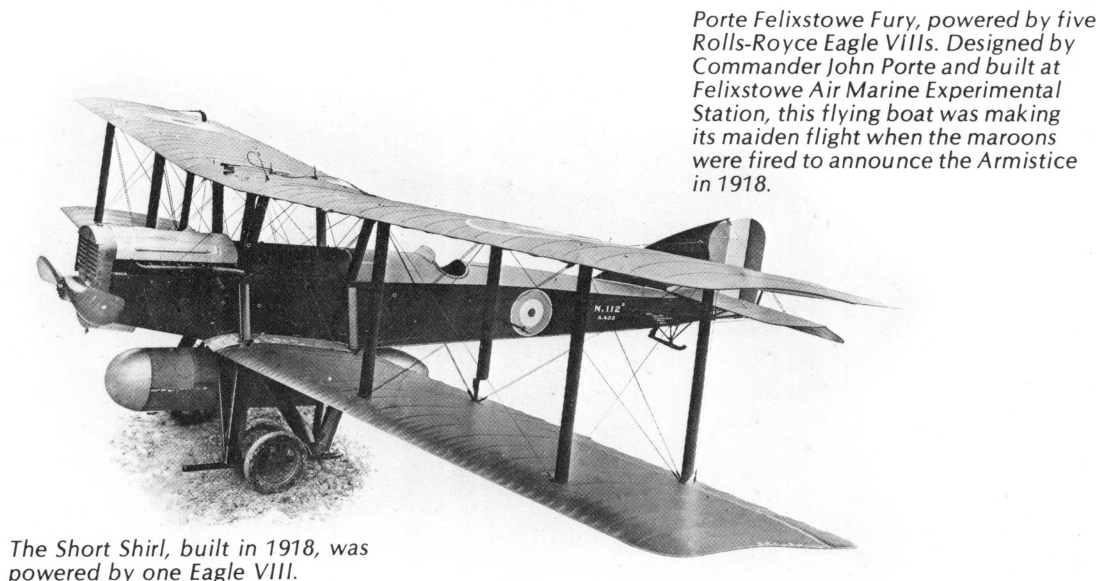

The Short Shirl, built in 1918, was powered by one Eagle VIII.

The Short landplane bomber was powered by the Eagle. This was one of the many aircraft types built in limited numbers during the war.

The Hawk was a small straight six-cylinder engine originally designed for trainer aircraft by Royce and his team. Unlike the Eagle, it drove the propeller directly without a reduction gearbox.

The Rolls-Royce Falcon III. The Falcon was a smaller engine than the Eagle and whereas the Eagle was primarily intended for bombers and seaplanes, the Falcon powered fighters, including the famous Bristol F2B (Brisfit). It was designed on Royce's instructions by R.W. Harvey-Bailey in Derby.

Rolls-Royce Condor Mark IV. The Condor was the last and largest of the family of Rolls-Royce aero-engines designed and developed in the First World War.

The Condor differed from its predecessors in having four valves per cylinder instead of two. Early Condors gave 650bhp. The Condor IV was specially developed for the Hawker Hornbill, which was the fastest fighter of its day. Unlike other Condors, the Mark IV had no propellor reduction gear, the propellor running at crankshaft speeds as high as 1,900 revolutions per minute.

Opposite: *The Shuttleworth Trust's Bristol F2B "Brisfit" fighter at Duxford in September 1979. The aeroplane is powered by a Falcon III; the oldest Rolls-Royce aero-engine still flying.*

the war had ended) while in various versions the engine also powered many other different types of aircraft.

In its day, the Falcon, which was Royce's own favourite engine (not designed by him, but by R.W. Harvey-Bailey at Derby), achieved a fame that was only to be equalled by the Merlin in the Spitfire and Hurricane fighters in the Battle of Britain in the Second World War. The Brisfit itself established a reputation for superiority in combat aircraft on both sides of the Western Front, its qualities eventually being grudgingly admitted by German fighter aces such as Manfred von Richthofen.

Collectively, these aero-engines from Rolls-Royce earned for themselves the same reputation for high-quality design, reliability and engineering integrity that the pre-war motor cars had achieved. A total of nearly 4,500 Eagle and Falcon engines had been delivered by the end of the war, and over 2,000 more were on contract. While it may be going too far to suggest that without the Rolls-Royce efforts Britain would not have won the war, there can be no doubt that Royce's own engineering genius was a powerful contribution to the ultimate victory.

The remaining engine emanating from Royce and his dedicated design team during the later years of the war was the bigger, 600hp Condor, also a derivative of the Eagle, but with some significant design changes. Although work began during the war, and it was intended for heavy bomber aircraft, this engine did not actually see active service. However, it found widespread uses in peace-time, both in military and civil aircraft well into the 1930s. One use was as the power-plant for the R-100 commercial airship.

British aircraft which were powered by the Condor included the Beardmore Inflexible; Avro Aldershot; Blackburn Iris I, II and III; de Havilland Derby; Fairey Atalanta, Titania and Freemantle; Handley Page Hardcross; Hawker Hornbill and Horsley; Saunders-Roe Valkyrie; Short Cromarty and Singapore; Vickers Vixen and Vanguard; and the Westland Yeovil.

Throughout the war, the company had inevitably expanded considerably in response to the national need. By the end of the war, the labour force had risen to 8,000, and the factory floor-space at Derby had extended from 30,500 square yards (25,502m^2) to about 58,000 square yards (48,495m^2).

In order to meet an emergency Rolls-Royce had greatly widened its industrial horizons, and had become a major force in British engineering. But even as the war came to an end, there was no real indication that Rolls-Royce was on the way to changing its character permanently.

A Sopwith triplane prototype, powered by a Rolls-Royce Eagle Mark I. Intended as a long range fighter, and carrying a pilot and two gunners, the aircraft was nicknamed the "Egg Box". Only one was built.

Opposite: *The gondola of a blimp. There were two classes of blimp, the single-engined SSZ class and the twin-engined SST. The picture shows an SSZ class. Note the Rolls-Royce Hawk engine, crew accommodation, voice tube between the open cockpits and the Lewis gun. The exhaust pipe is fitted with a fishtail similar to that fitted on Rolls-Royce motor cars.*

3 BETWEEN THE WARS

The first few years of peace required extensive readjustment. Although after some time there was inevitably a cut-back in the company's activities, temporarily the work-load remained high, pending the run-down of war-time contracts, and the initial outlook seemed bright. The company returned as swiftly as possible to motor-car production, and although many of its markets had been lost as a result of the war, it still had a waiting list of customers, including some from pre-war days.

A 1926 Phantom open tourer with body by Hooper.

However, it was the beginning of a time of severe economic hardship for many. Over the next few years, although Rolls-Royce remained profitable, it experienced some difficult times, with slackening demand for its products as the Depression deepened. The company also had to adjust to changes in management. Ernest Claremont died in 1921, and was replaced as chairman by Sir Edward Goulding (later Lord Wargrave) who had been on the board of directors since 1913. Claude Johnson was also to die suddenly from pneumonia in 1926, aged sixty-two, wearied after his strenuous efforts in America to establish manufacture of parts for the Eagle and then motor-car production at Springfield, Massachusetts, at a time of intensifying competition, both in that country and at home.

Despite its war-time achievements in the aero-engine field, the company regarded itself still very much as a motor-car manufacturer. In the early 1920s, the board decided that it would be wise to build a smaller, less expensive car in addition to continuing with the Silver Ghost, since it was feared that the company would not be able to survive on demand for the bigger, vehicle alone. Thus, the 20hp model emerged in October, 1922. It was to remain in production until 1929, during which time 2,940 were built. From 1906 to 1925, no less than 7,876 chassis for Silver Ghosts were built, of which 6,173 came from Manchester and Derby and the rest, 1,703, from the Springfield, Massachusetts, factory.

Eventually, it became apparent that the Silver Ghost would have to be superceded, and the 40/50hp Phantom I emerged in 1925. Between 1925 and 1929, when the Phantom II emerged, 2,212 Phantom Is were built at Derby, with another 1,240 being built at Springfield, up to 1931.

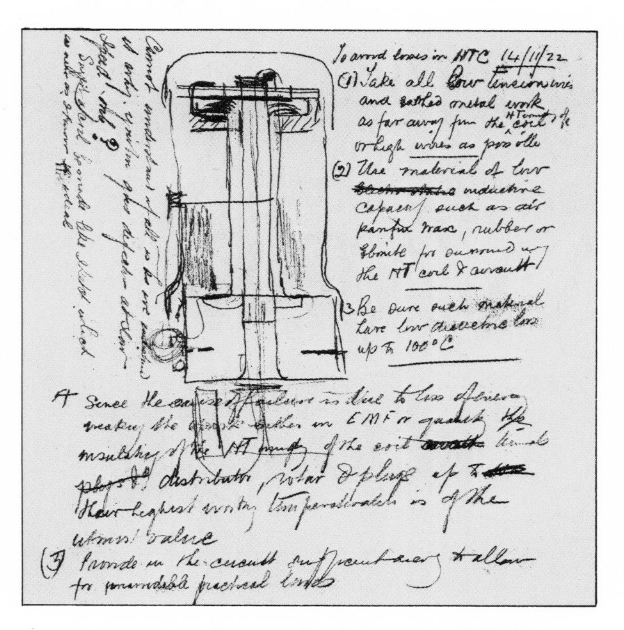

One of Sir Henry Royce's personal sketches for a motor-car electrical ignition coil.

Sir Henry Royce outside his home, Villa Mimosa at Le Canadel near St. Tropez on the south coast of France. He is seen talking to Sir James Percy beside an experimental 40/50hp Phantom II.

The Eagle IX was Rolls-Royce's first civil aero-engine. Carburettors were mounted low to allow gravity fuel-feed and avoid the dangers of a pressurised fuel system.

The unsupercharged Kestrel 1B. The Kestrel represented a new generation of aero-engines when it appeared in the late 1920s. Many Kestrels were supercharged to improve altitude performance and they were the first Rolls-Royce engines to incorporate this feature.

Opposite: *Vickers Vimy production at Morgans works, Linslade in April 1918. Nine Eagle VIII engines are visible in the picture.*

Even as competition in motor cars intensified, life was becoming just as difficult in the aero-engine field. From 1919 onwards, the first airlines began to emerge in Europe. A large number of dramatic short and long-range pioneering civil flights occurred, demonstrating that a new era of civil air travel was dawning.

Many of these important flights were carried out with aircraft using Rolls-Royce Eagle engines, but although development of these continued, no new aero-engine ventures were begun by the company for some time. There was as yet no requirement for a new aero-engine specifically for civil purposes, while in the military field, the government, faced with substantial war stocks and no need for heavy arms spending, was disinclined to encourage new aircraft and engine development. Thus, the company kept its aviation activities alive in the early post-war period by the sale of Eagle, Falcon and Condor engines to civil and military operators, the latter mainly overseas, and by the repair of existing engines and by sales of spares.

One of the most dramatic of these post-war pioneering flights that kept the public's interest in aviation alive, was the first non-stop crossing of the Atlantic Ocean. The flight, from Newfoundland to Clifden, in Ireland, by John Alcock and Arthur Whitten Brown took place over the 14th and 15th June, 1919, in the twin-Eagle VIII-powered Vickers Vimy. They covered the 1,890 miles (3,042kms) in a total time of 16 hours and 27 minutes, one of the greatest achievements in the annals of aviation.

Eventually, it was Royce himself, now over sixty and still active despite the recurrent ill-health that obliged him to winter at Le Canadel, who decided that the company should embark on a new aero-engine programme. He was aided by A.G. Elliott (who was eventually to succeed him as chief engineer) while the design team had also been strengthened by the arrival of A.J. Rowledge, who had originally worked for the Napier engine company, designing the rival Lion engine.

Although there were some small government engine contracts; for example, one for limited Condor production, it was a period of fierce competition. Rolls-Royce's main rivals were

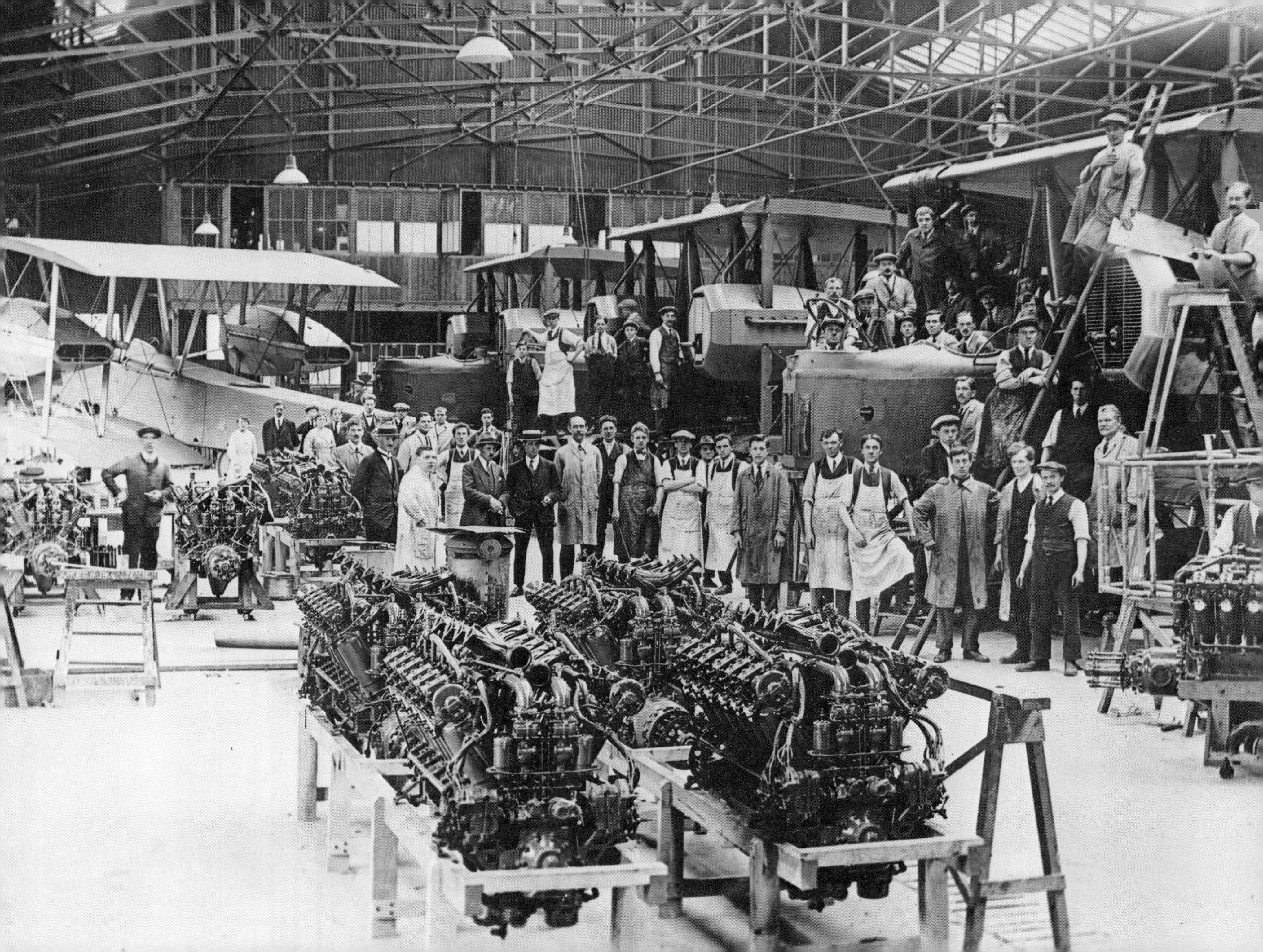

Above left: *One of the Eagle VIII engines from Alcock and Brown's transatlantic Vickers Vimy.* Above: *Alcock and Brown's landing at the end of the first direct transatlantic flight in June 1919. They mistook an Irish bog for a green field, with sad consequences for their Vickers Vimy. The aircraft is preserved in the Science Museum in London.*

Napier, Bristol and Armstrong Siddeley, all in the hunt for orders.

In 1927 Rolls-Royce produced the "F" engine (later to be called the Kestrel). It was to become the power-unit of many RAF fighters in the late 1920s and early 1930s, including one of the most famous of that time, the Hawker Fury. Then, in 1928, with the "F" series still under development and production, a larger and more powerful "H" engine, later renamed the Buzzard, also emerged. This engine found a variety of uses, particularly, but by no means exclusively, in flying-boats, such as the Blackburn Iris and Short Singapore.

Late in the 1920s there occurred yet another of those turning points in the company's history, through its association with the famous international Schneider Trophy races, the Blue Riband of air competitions. The Schneider Trophy was first presented to the Aero Club de France in December, 1912, by Jacques Schneider, a pioneer aviator and racing motorist. He intended it to promote the sound design and operational dependability of seaplanes. Inevitably, however, the races became imbued with nationalistic overtones. The rules specified that the country or aero club which won the race three times out of five consecutive attempts could retain the Trophy in perpetuity, and so the races became very much a matter of nationalistic pride, rather than technical and sporting endeavour.

Britain won the second race, at Monaco in 1914, with Howard Pixton flying a Sopwith Tabloid at 86.78mph (139·65km/h). Britain also won the sixth race at Naples in 1922, with Henri Biard flying a Supermarine Sea Lion II using a Napier Lion engine, at a speed of 145·7mph (234·47km/h). In 1927, Britain won again, at Venice in a Supermarine S-5, with a Napier Lion

Opposite: *A replica of a Vickers Vimy bomber built by enthusiasts at the British Aircraft Corporation. Rolls-Royce restored two old Eagle Mark IX engines for the aeroplane (they should authentically have been Mark VIII) and found that on test the engines were within 2hp of their original test performance when new.*

Reginald Mitchell with Henry Royce at Calshot in 1929. Mitchell designed the S6 seaplane and Royce was responsible for its "R" engine. Mitchell was later to design the Spitfire, powered by the Merlin.

engine of 875hp, flown by Flight Lieutenant S.N. Webster of the RAF High Speed Flight on 26th September, at an average speed of 281·65mph (453·26km/h).

For the next contest, at Calshot (Spithead) in 1929, Reginald J. Mitchell, of the Vickers-Supermarine Aviation Works, wanted a bigger engine, and in the autumn of 1928 Rolls-Royce was asked by the Air Ministry to build it. The managing director of the company, Basil Johnson (who had succeeded his brother, Claude) at first declined, but Royce himself decided otherwise, strongly supported by Ernest Hives, Cyril Lovesey and A.J. Rowledge. The three men visited Royce at West Wittering on a beautiful autumn morning, and all four went for a walk along the beach. When Royce was tired they sat by a groyne and Royce sketched the engine design in the sand

A Supermarine Sea Eagle of the early 1920s, powered by the Eagle IX engine.

with his walking-stick, raking it out as changes were suggested. Thus, a major new aero-engine venture was born, and from that morning walk great events were to flow.

Work began on converting the Buzzard, and by the time of the race at Spithead on the 6th and 7th September, 1929, the resulting engine, called the "R" engine, of 1,900hp, was ready.

This was a magnificent achievement in its own right, for some severe technical problems had been encountered in the final stages of development, not the least being valve distortion and burning, and plug sooting. These problems were overcome in work of unparalleled intensity by the Rolls-Royce team, headed by Cyril Lovesey and aided by Francis Rodwell Banks. Banks (later an Air Commodore) was a fuel specialist, working with the Anglo-American Oil company. He produced a special "fuel cocktail" for the Supermarine aircraft that indubitably helped it through to final victory. Rod Banks was later to play a major role in aero-engine development in Britain, and he is still active today.

Britain won the 1929 race, with Flying Officer H.R.D. Waghorn piloting the Supermarine S-6 at an average speed of 328·63mph (528·86km/h). The course passed close to Royce's home at West Wittering. A few days later, on 12th September, the same aircraft, this time flown by Squadron Leader A.H. Orlebar, raised the world absolute speed record to 357·7mph (575·65km/h).

One result of these achievements was the award of a baronetcy to Royce himself, which he characteristically tried to play down, although it clearly gave him great pleasure, and which everyone else agreed was a long overdue honour.

In 1931, the Schneider Trophy race came round again. But it was the time of the Depression, and the government felt that, because of the economic situation, the contest could not be supported officially. This caused a considerable rumpus, and the government came under vigorous attack in the press and Parliament. Then, Lady Lucy Houston, the widow of a shipping magnate, came forward with £100,000 of her own money to support the race. She castigated the government so fiercely that the decision was reversed.

The delay all this had caused left no time to create a new engine to the higher power required by the competition. So the "R" engine was put back into development. After another period of intense activity by the technicians in the Rolls-Royce experimental department, headed by Ernest Hives, and with further help from Rod Banks on fuel, the Supermarine S-6B was fitted

A Supermarine S6 of the 1929 Schneider Trophy race, powered by the "R" engine.

Flight Lieutenant G.H. Stainforth poses with the "R" engine with which he took the world air speed record at 407.5mph (655.78km/h) in 1931. The engine is about to be returned to Derby on a modified Phantom car.

Lady Houston at the scene of the 1931 Schneider Trophy race. Her generous guarantee of £100,000 made British participation possible during the country's difficult economic times.

with an "R" engine of 2,350hp. Piloted by Flight Lieutenant J.N. Boothman of the High Speed Flight of the RAF, it won the Trophy outright for Britain with no challengers, at an average speed of 340·08mph (547·29km/h), again at Spithead, on 13th September, 1931.

On the same day, Flight Lieutenant G.H. Stainforth, also of the High Speed Flight, used the S-6B to put the world absolute speed record up to 379·05mph (610km/h). A few days later, on 29th September, with the "R" engine further boosted to 2,550hp, he put the record up again to 407·5mph (655·78km/h) thus attaining what Ernest Hives regarded as "the mark that matters" – 400mph (643·72km/h). Royce heard of these achievements as he lay ill in bed at West Wittering.

The "R" engine was also subsequently used to establish several new land and water speed records. Sir Malcolm Campbell used it in his *Bluebird* racing car to set up a new land speed record of over 272mph (437·72km/h) at Daytona Beach, Florida, subsequently raising it further to 301mph (484·39km/h). It was also used by Sir Henry Segrave and Kay Don in the *Miss England* high-speed boat, while Captain George Eyston used two "R" engines including one from the successful 1931 S-6B for his record-breaking car, *Thunderbolt*, putting the land speed record up to 357·5mph (575·32km/h).

The importance of the Schneider Trophy and its associated air speed record ventures to Rolls-Royce, Vickers-Supermarine and to Britain should never be under-estimated. Many new technical developments in aircraft and aero-engines resulted from the challenge the Trophy posed to Royce and his dedicated team, and to R.J. Mitchell (who died in 1936) and his team at Supermarine.

Sir Malcolm Campbell's Bluebird *world speed record car, powered by the "R" engine.*

Arthur Sidgreaves, who had by then succeded Basil Johnson as the managing director of Rolls-Royce, was in no doubt of the importance of the races. After the 1931 race he wrote: "As a result of the test this year all the main components of these engines have undergone a definite improvement, and in consequence the life of the standard engine in service will be much longer than it would otherwise have been. From the development point of view, the Schneider Trophy contest is almost an economy, because it saves so much time in arriving at certain technical improvements. It is not too much to say that research for the Schneider Trophy contest over the past two years is what our aero-engine department would otherwise have taken six to ten years to learn. For the last few years Britain's supremacy in the manufacture of aircraft is generally recognised, and is due to the experience and knowledge gained in contests such as that for the Schneider Trophy." From these Schneider Trophy efforts were to emerge

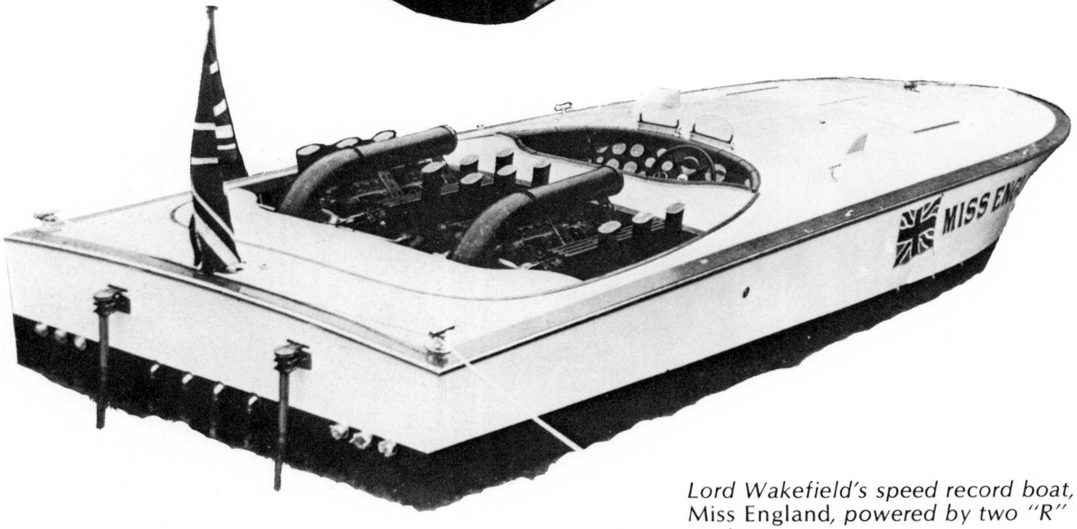

Lord Wakefield's speed record boat, Miss England*, powered by two "R" engines.*

Preparing for the Schneider Trophy. On the left of the picture is Cyril Lovesey, one of the greatest Rolls-Royce development engineers. He contributed to the success of every engine from the Kestrel to the RB211. Throughout the war he was in charge of Merlin development.

eventually two matchless pieces of engineering that were to be crucial to Britain in the Second World War – the Merlin engine and the Spitfire.

Also at this time, another major aircraft designer, Sydney Camm, at Hawker Aircraft, was designing the Hurricane which also used the Merlin, and partnered the Spitfire in the Battle of Britain.

Following the Schneider victory, Rolls-Royce, as a private venture, began late in 1932 to develop a new engine, initally of 1,000hp, based on all the knowledge and experience gained on the "R" engine. Design work began immediately, and the first complete engine was ready to start tests in October 1933. Known initially as PV-12 (for private venture) it was entirely the work of Royce's team, for the great man was now increasingly ill. Only after it had successfully completed its initial trials was it taken up by the Air Ministry, at which stage it received its name, the Merlin.

Royce himself did not live to see the fruits of these endeavours. Worn out by a life-time of unremitting engineering endeavour, and weakened by frequent bouts of ill-health, he died on 22nd April, 1933, at West Wittering. He was seventy, and the last of the four great pioneers of the company to die, after Rolls, Claremont and Johnson. He had always shunned publicity: "I am only a mechanic," he would say. Nevertheless, he left behind a legacy of quality in engineering that has never been surpassed, and his name has become synonymous with reliability, integrity and durability in automobile and aero-engine design.

The achievement of engineering excellence was his only goal, and he sought it all his life. He had once coined the phrase: "Whatever is rightly done, however humble, is noble". It was carved over his fireplace at his West Wittering home, a

A Short Sarafand powered by no less than six Buzzards mounted end-to-end in pairs.

most memorable epitaph to his own life's work.

Legend has it that after Royce's death, the insignia "R-R" on the radiator badges of all Rolls-Royce cars was painted in black, instead of red as previously, and this practice persists to this day. Unfortunately this appealing story is not true. Royce himself had authorised the change three years before his death.

After Royce's death, the tempo of work on the Merlin engines accelerated rapidly into the mid-1930s, as the international situation worsened and the likelihood of war increased. Manufacture of Merlins now took precedence over that of the motor-cars. The company's path had dramatically changed. It was irretrievably linked with the aviation industry, and motor-cars, although still regarded as important were nevertheless relegated to second place.

By the time war was declared in September, 1939, the Merlin had become Britain's most important aero-engine, and it was fitted into not only the Spitfire and the Hurricane, but also the

Armstrong Whitworth Whitley and Fairey Battle bombers. The list of subsequent aircraft that it eventually powered reads almost like an inventory of the RAF's total aircraft fleet during the Second World War.

During the years leading up to the war, there were many major management changes. In 1936 Lord Wargrave retired and was succeeded as chairman by Lord Herbert Scott, who had joined the company before the First World War. Ernest Hives, who had been with Rolls and then was one of the early members of the Royce team, was appointed works manager, in succession to Arthur Wormald, and it was on him that the burden of boosting Merlin production was to fall.

However, the motor-car activities of the company had not been ignored in the 1930s. The 20/25hp model emerged in 1929 as a companion to the 40/50hp Phantom II of the same year. Two events dominated this side of the company's activities. One was the closure of the Springfield works in the USA, in the face of intensifying competition and mass production from the American motor manufacturers.

The other was the acquisition in 1931 of the famous Bentley Motor Company, which had run into financial difficulties. Thereafter, the famous Bentley "silent sports cars" were built by Rolls-Royce. The Phantom III emerged in 1935, and this was followed by the 25/30hp model in 1936, while the Wraith made its appearance in 1938.

These years also saw a number of other significant developments. In 1934, the company moved in with the RAF at Hucknall, near Nottingham to develop the Rolls-Royce flight test centre, initially under Cyril Lovesey and largely at Hives' instigation, to meet the growing demands of Merlin engine development. Hucknall was to expand considerably thereafter, and filled an indispensable role in the company's activities, especi-

A 1937 Phantom III. When it was launched in 1935, the new 40/50 model was the most technically advanced car in the world.

The Rolls-Royce Hucknall flying circus circa 1937. Left to right: Fairey Battle, Hawker Horsley, Whitney Straight, Heinkel He70, and various Hawker biplanes of the Hart, Audax, Demon and Fury families.

ally during the Second World War and immediately thereafter.

The inexorable onset of war was reflected in the spectacular growth of the company. From 1919 to 1931, the number of employees fluctuated according to periods of economic boom and depression, and at one stage it had fallen to as low as 3,000. But through the 1930s, under the influence of rising demand for military aero-engines, it rose steadily. By 1936, there were 6,900, and by 1939, 12,500 employees, with additional Merlin "shadow" factories at Crewe (from 1938) and Hillington, Glasgow, (1939) as well as the main factory at Nightingale Road, Derby.

Also in this period, the determined and distinctive stamp of Ernest Hives was increasingly felt in all the company's activities. He was eventually to become chairman and managing director, and it was he, more than any other man, who was to dominate the affairs of Rolls-Royce through the ensuing turbulent and testing years of war, and eventually also into the peace beyond. His blunt approach and sharp tongue were not to everyone's liking. He often said he regarded work as: "The best fun on earth, and working for Rolls-Royce is even better!" But he was a first-rate engineer, and his close association with Rolls and Royce from pre-World War One days had imbued him with meticulous persistence in the pursuit of engineering excellence. He was tough upon, but well liked by, the tightly-knit team he built up around him, who were to serve him and the country well in the difficult days that lay ahead.

4 WORLD WAR TWO

The Second World War found Rolls-Royce fully occupied with Merlin engine production, initially for Spitfire and Hurricane fighters.

Every effort was now being concentrated on this engine, and development work on other advanced prototypes, for example, the Exe, was discontinued. For the company believed that the Merlin could be developed much further to meet growing military requirements for higher power ratings, apart from the immediately urgent need for maximum quantity production. The company's belief ultimately proved correct, for by the end of the war, the power of the Merlin had been doubled to over 2,000hp and at all stages of the war the Merlin kept ahead of comparable German piston-engined developments in power and high-altitude performance.

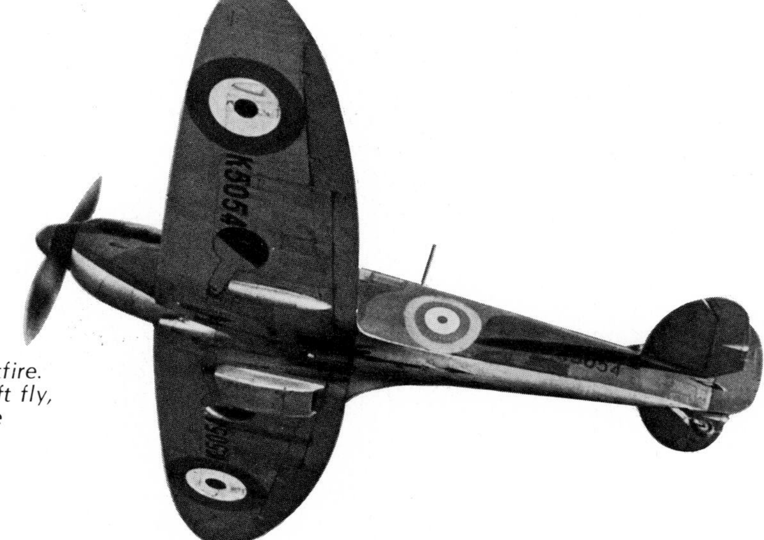

The prototype Supermarine Spitfire. Mitchell lived to see this aircraft fly, but died before the first Spitfire squadron was formed.

Rolls-Royce, under Ernest Hives, was working a seven-day week, and because of this intense concentration upon production, during the Battle of Britain the company was able to ensure that all the Spitfires and Hurricanes of the RAF were equipped with Merlins.

As the demand for the Merlin increased, with more and more RAF aircraft of different types using it, the Ford Motor Company at Manchester and the Packard Company in the USA were brought in to help with production.

The Merlin powered the famous Lancaster

heavy bomber, and another of the most significant uses for the engine was in the North American P-51 Mustang fighter, a combination that ensured fighter cover for Allied bombers all the way to Berlin and back, revolutionising the daylight bombing of Germany. The Mustang/Merlin combination has been described as the most aerodynamically perfect fighter ever built, even better in many pilot's views than the Spitfire. In all, 15,582 Merlin/Mustangs were built, and they were in service with many air forces well into the 1960s.

The quintet of Spitfire, Hurricane, Mosquito, the Merlin-powered Mustang and the Lancaster probably did more than any other aircraft to help to win the war – although the Merlin in fact powered many other types of aeroplane, and in all, over 166,000 Merlin engines were built.

The Merlin engine served not only in the air, but also on land, in tanks (where it was known as the Meteor engine), and at sea in motor-torpedo boats, gunboats and air-sea rescue craft.

The development of the Merlin for use in tanks was undertaken by the company's motor-car engineers, who also became responsible eventually for developing the tanks as well. The Meteor/Merlin tank engine was in service for years after the war with the British Army. The same team developed a new range of military petrol engines, called the "B" range, which were also to grow in importance after the war. Design and development work was also carried out by Rolls-Royce during the war on automatic cannons and machine guns, the production of the cannon being undertaken by another company.

The close relationship that evolved during the war, and especially during the Battle of Britain, between Rolls-Royce and the RAF is recognised by the famous Battle of Britain

The Merlin. Over 160,000 were built by Rolls-Royce in Derby, Crewe and Glasgow, by Ford at Trafford Park and by Packard in the USA.

The North American P-51 Mustang. Originally powered by an American engine, the P-51 was re-engined with the Merlin and became one of the most successful piston-engined fighters of all time. The picture shows one of the first experimental engine conversions carried out by Rolls-Royce at Hucknall.

A Hurricane of the RAF Battle of Britain Memorial Flight.

A magnificently restored Spitfire at Duxford in September 1979.

Opposite: *Rolls-Royce's own Spitfire XIV powered by a Griffon 65.*

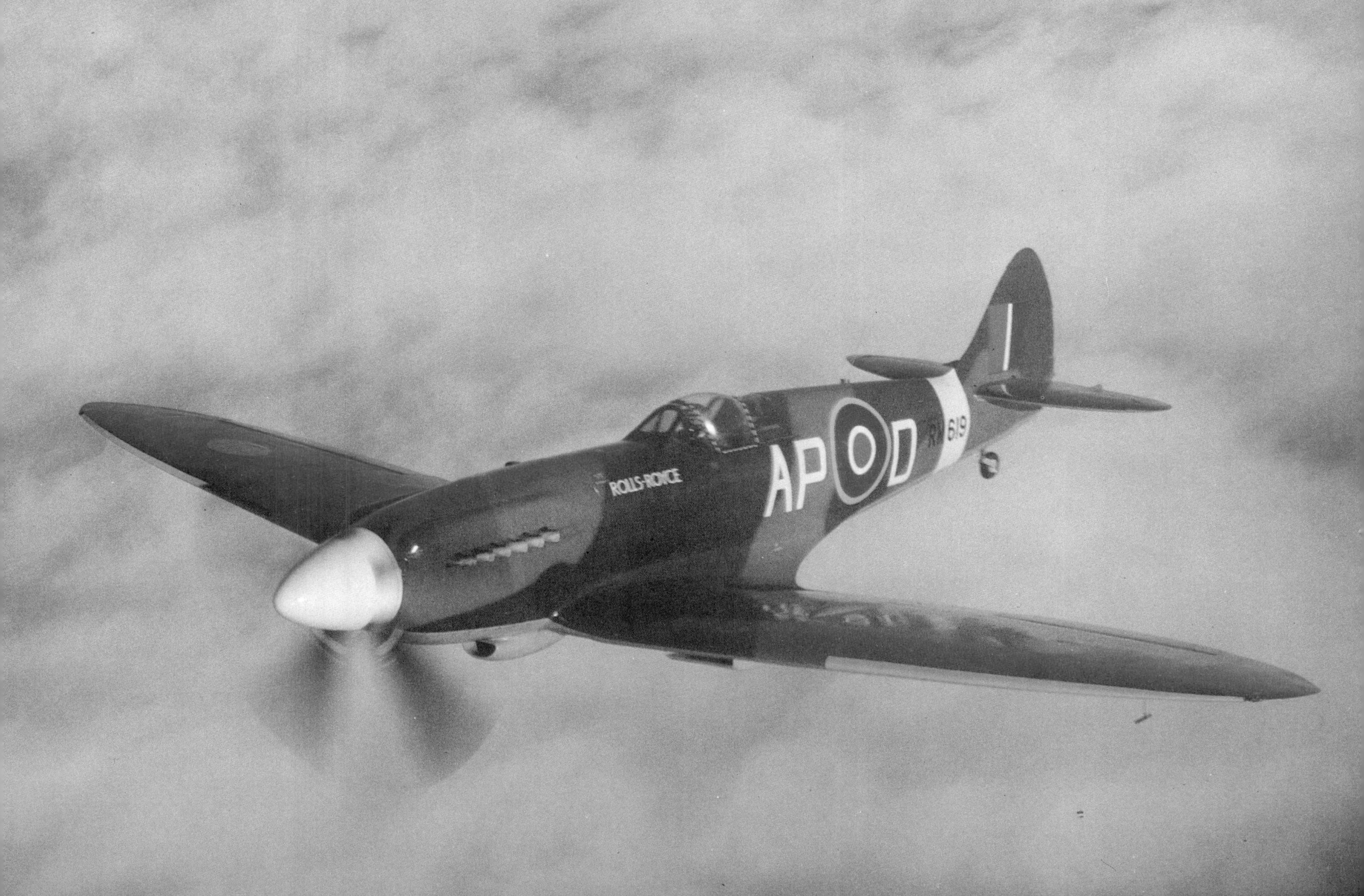
ROLLS-ROYCE
AP D

Some marks of the Vickers Wellington bomber were powered by the Merlin.

The de Havilland Mosquito, powered by two Merlins. Built of wood, the Mosquito was a very fast and versatile aircraft. It was used as a bomber, fighter, "pathfinder" and for photo-reconnaissance.

window, in the main entrance hall of the works in Nightingale Road. This bears the inscription: "This window commemorates the pilots of the Royal Air Force who in the Battle of Britain turned the work of our hands into the salvation of our country".

The massive expansion of Merlin production is reflected in the equally dramatic growth of the company's labour force, which reached a peak of 55,600 in 1943 – more than four times the 1939 level.

The Merlin was not the only piston engine built by Rolls-Royce during the war. The Griffon, a bigger engine than the Merlin, had been started in late 1939, but work on it had been held up to allow for maximum effort on the Merlin. When the Griffon programme was resumed, the engine was developed quickly, primarily for use by the Fleet Air Arm, and before the end of the war it was being used in later versions of the Spitfire and Seafire, and the Fairey Firefly and Barracuda.

After the war development of the engine continued, especially for the Avro Shackleton long-range maritime reconnaissance and anti-submarine warfare aircraft.

Among other wartime engines was the 24-cylinder Vulture, which was used in the twin-engined Avro Manchester bomber, the Hawker Tornado fighter, and the Vickers-Armstrongs Warwick bomber, but it was soon discontinued, again so as to concentrate upon the Merlin.

Another significant late war-time engine was called "Eagle the Second", which was begun when it became apparent that an engine of higher power than the Merlin would be useful. This engine was initiated late in 1942, at a rating of 3,500hp, and it went into the prototype Westland Wyvern deck-landing strike aircraft. But towards the end of the war it was becoming apparent, as a result of the rapid strides made with another new engine development, that the piston engine's days were likely to be numbered. As a result comparatively few "Eagle the Second" power-plants were built.

Work had been under way in secret for some time on a revolutionary new propulsion system, the jet engine.

As early as the late 1920s, ideas for this type of power-unit for aircraft had been publicly mooted, without attracting any significant interest. Dr A.A. Griffith, who was eventually to become the chief scientist of the company, had written a paper about gas-turbines in 1929, whilst still at the Royal Aircraft Establishment, Farnborough.

Even earlier, however, in 1928, a young RAF officer, Frank Whittle (later to become Air Commodore Sir Frank Whittle) had published his fundamental thesis on the gas-turbine as a power-plant for aircraft, following studies conducted in

The Hillington factory in Glasgow worked night and day to build Merlin engines during the war. More women were employed in Glasgow than in other factories. Hives' message to the workforce was, "work till it hurts".

The Luftwaffe certainly knew where the Hillington factory was. This is a Luftwaffe reconnaissance photograph. However, Rolls-Royce escaped lightly from bombing. Derby was hit once by a lone raider and Crewe once.

the early to mid-1920s. His work was based on the centrifugal-flow system, and he took out his first patents in 1930. Despite great financial and other difficulties, and in the face of official disinterest, he successfully ran his first engine on the test-bed on 12th April, 1937.

Rolls-Royce itself set up an office in 1938 to study gas-turbine technology, and Dr Griffith joined the company in 1939 to work on his own ideas in this field.

By late 1939, it was clear to officialdom that Whittle's ideas had reached the point where a practicable aircraft-propulsion unit was possible. The Air Ministry had by then given its belated support, and Whittle was also aided by Rover. Whittle had set up a company called Power Jets and was pushing ahead on what was to become the Whittle W-1 engine, while the Gloster Aircraft Company was at work on a suitable airframe. The Gloster E28/39 experimental aircraft, using the Whittle W-1, made a successful maiden flight in secret from RAF Cranwell on the evening of 15th May, 1941, piloted by P.E.G. Sayer, Gloster's chief test pilot.

By that time, however, Rolls-Royce was also making components for the W-1. Dr (later Sir) Stanley Hooker, another of the great engineers who served Rolls-Royce for many years (and who eventually went to Bristol Aero-Engines, later renamed Bristol Siddeley Engines), tells how in the summer of 1940 he convinced Ernest Hives that the Whittle jet engine was worthy of his consideration. They went to see Whittle, who at that time was working in a disused iron foundry in Lutterworth, near Rugby, with limited personnel, money and facilities.

Hooker recalls: "He (Whittle) laid down the performance and the aerodynamic design of the jet engine with the precision of Newton. And

The Heinkel He70 bought by Rolls-Royce for its clean aerodynamic shape in the 1930s. It was used for flight testing high speed engine installations at Hucknall.

even today we still use his formulae for the calculation of the performance of jet engines. I was very impressed with his work." So was Hives. Whittle told him he was short of turbine blades and other parts, and Hives said: "Send us the drawings and we'll make the parts for you".

Rolls-Royce eventually took over the development of the entire engine. Stanley Hooker tells how this occurred: "Hives said to me: 'We're going to have dinner with S.P. Wilkes, the chairman of the Rover company, tonight in Clitheroe'. And so we went and after dinner, Hives turned to Wilkes and said, 'Look, what are you doing with this jet aero-engine? You're not an aero-engine company. You grub about on the ground!' I remember the phrase. 'I'll tell you what I'll do. I'll give you our tank-engine factory at Nottingham. You give me this jet job in Yorkshire.' And Wilkes said 'Done!' And so we took over the facility which had been set up for the

Opposite: *The memorial window to the pilots of the Battle of Britain in the Rolls-Royce works at Derby.*

The W2B/23 Welland turbojet. This was the first Rolls-Royce turbojet to go into production. It powered early Gloster Meteor fighters, the only jet aircraft to see active service with the Allies during the Second World War.

Engines being built within Derby main works during the late 1940s. Merlin and Eagle piston engines are on the right alongside Derwent and Nene jet engines.

manufacture of the Whittle jet engine. It was an old spinning mill, housing about 2,000 people. And I was sent there as chief engineer to get this project into production . . . As a consequence, within a few months, Rolls-Royce were able to put 2,000 men and all the facilities of Rolls-Royce onto the job of making Whittle's jet engine work. And I'm happy to say that after we took over the job, within six months we had the engine tested at its designed thrust of 1,600lbs (725·75kg). This was the W-2B." Hooker was assisted by a brilliant young engineer from Rover, Adrian Lombard, who remained with Rolls-Royce until his death in the late 1960s.

After further flight trials in the Gloster E-28/39, and in the tails of two Wellington bombers, the engine went into production for the twin-engined Gloster Meteor fighter. The Rolls-Royce-Whittle W-2B/23 engine was renamed the Welland – which started the practice of calling Rolls-Royce jet engines after rivers (to give the idea of "flow" associated with jet propulsion).

Initially powered by the Welland, the twin-engined Gloster Meteor went into service with the RAF in July 1944, the only Allied jet aircraft to see active fighting before the war ended. One of its first operational tasks was to fight off the German V-1 Flying Bombs launched against Britain that summer. Meteor pilots found they could fly alongside the V-1s, get their wing-tips under those of the V-1s, and tilt the bombs upside down so that they crashed into the sea.

The Meteor was to become one of the world's greatest jet aeroplanes; with more than 3,800 being built in the UK and in Holland and Belgium between 1944 and 1954.

Following the development of the basic Welland, Rolls-Royce went on to develop the Derwent, Nene and Tay series of engines, all of which proved a great success in British, American and French military aircraft from the mid-1940s and up to the late 1950s.

The Derwent in all its versions was a particularly successful engine, with over 9,700 being built in Britain and Belgium before production ended in 1954. This engine was used in many versions of the Meteor fighter. A more powerful engine, the Derwent 5 went into the Meteor and enabled new world air speed records in excess of 600mph (965·60km/h) to be achieved in the immediate post-war period by the re-established RAF High Speed Flight. On 7th November, 1945, Group Captain H.J. "Willie" Wilson flying a Meteor F.Mk. III, set a record of 606·26mph (975·68km/h) at Herne Bay. On 7th September, 1946, Group Captain E.M. "Teddy" Donaldson raised it to 615·78mph (991km/h) at Tangmere, flying a Meteor F.Mk. IV.

The Nene engine went into the Hawker Sea Hawk, the Supermarine Attacker, the American Lockheed Shooting Star and other US combat aircraft, and Vampires for Australia.

The Welland engine was flight-tested by Rolls-Royce in the tail of a Wellington bomber at Hucknall.

The Gloster Meteor, powered by the Derwent. The Meteor was one of the most successful of the new generation of jet fighters. It entered service with the Royal Air Force in 1944. In 1945 and again in 1946 it took the world's air speed record.

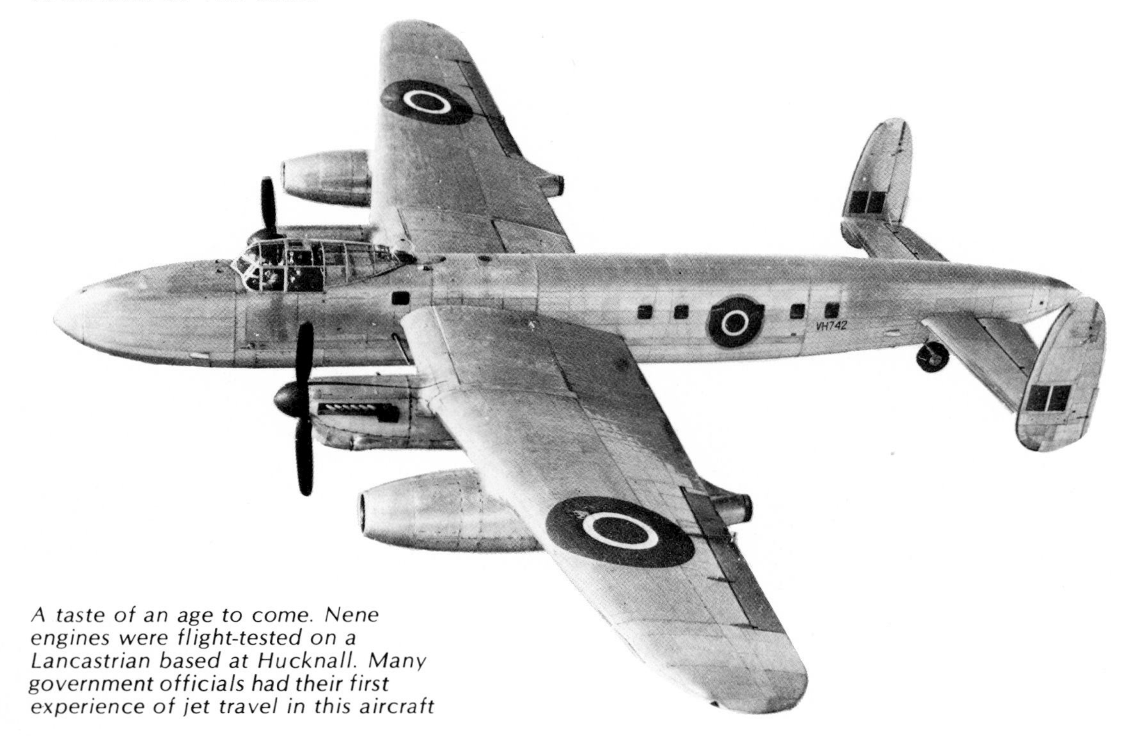

A taste of an age to come. Nene engines were flight-tested on a Lancastrian based at Hucknall. Many government officials had their first experience of jet travel in this aircraft

A Management meeting in the old boardroom in the main works at Derby during the second World War. Among those shown are Sir Arthur Sidgreaves, Ernest Hives, Tommy Haldenby and Cyril Lovesey.

Opposite: *The last Avro Lancaster of the Royal Air Force flies over RAF Cranwell, accompanied by a Spitfire (left) and Hurricane (right). These aircraft are from the RAF Battle of Britain Memorial Flight. All of them are powered by Merlin engines.*

Britain's jet-engine expertise was given to the USA in 1941, and this enabled General Electric to develop a jet engine of its own very quickly. This was the GE1-A, which powered the first US jet aircraft, the Bell XP-59A Airacomet, which made its maiden flight at Muroc Dry Lake, California, (later to be named Edwards Air Force Base) on 2nd October, 1942.

The Tay engine was also developed from the basic Nene engine by Rolls-Royce and then, after the war, by Pratt & Whitney of the USA as the J-48 engine for various combat aircraft. It was also developed by Hispano-Suiza of France for early Dassault Mystére fighters. The Nene was also made available to Russia by the post-war Labour Government, which enabled that country to get into the military jet aircraft business very much more rapidly than might otherwise have been the case, and the Russians in turn passed the technological details over to the Chinese.

Thus, work that began in the UK was very swiftly disseminated round the world, largely as a result of the exigencies of war-time politics, but to the longer-term financial detriment of the UK government and Rolls-Royce who might otherwise have secured business worth many hundreds of millions of pounds over the ensuing years.

When the war ended, Merlin and Griffon piston engines were still being produced in large quantities, and indeed were to provide the company with much business for years to come. The Avro Shackleton is still in RAF service today as an anti-submarine and airborne early warning (AEW) aircraft, powered by four Griffon engines.

By early 1945, however, it was clear to Hives and the top-management team in the company that a new era had dawned that was likely to change the shape of world civil and military aviation, and with it the future of Rolls-Royce.

5 INTO A NEW ERA

The immediate post-war period, like that after the First World War, was one of readjustment, a painful one for some, in that the work-force was reduced from 55,000 to about 30,000 in just fifteen months.

It was also a period of exciting challenge, later to be marred by a series of political and technical errors which undid much of the work done by the aerospace industry's designers, and slowed British aircraft, and engine development.

Initially, however, it was clear that the advent of the gas-turbine engine had virtually rendered the piston-engined aircraft obsolete for most military duties, and seemed likely in time to do the same for civil airliners. As a result, the next 15 years saw Rolls-Royce moving into a wide range of new civil and military engines, broadening the spectrum of its activities as knowledge and experience with the gas-turbine engine itself evolved rapidly.

This period was also to see some dramatic changes in demand for aerospace products. The cutbacks in production and development programmes following the Second World War were replaced by a new rearmament programme in 1953, in which aviation was given top priority, resulting in the development of new military aircraft and engines.

Aviation dominated the company's thinking. Although motor cars remained important, they were now an adjunct to the mainstream of the company's business.

Changes were overtaking the company in other ways. Although the top team which had seen the company through the war, under the leadership of Ernest Hives, was still dedicated to the pursuit of engineering excellence, it was much less of a tightly-knit family than it had been at the beginning of the war. This was largely because the company's very substantial growth had made it impossible for the top management to sustain, beyond all but a small immediate number of personnel, the kind of intimate personal relationships which had been part of the pre-war Rolls-Royce tradition.

While at the top much of this relationship still prevailed, the company, under the influence of rising demand for its products, had begun to change its face, to become less paternalistic and more of an internationally-orientated industrial giant concern.

For Ernest Hives, or simply "Hs" as he was known throughout the company, the reward for his war-time endeavours came with a barony on 16th June, 1950. Hives had declined a knighthood earlier in the war, but had been made a Companion of Honour in 1943. Commenting on his peerage, Hives in a message to the work-force said: "It is my wish that the great honour which has been conferred upon me by His Majesty should be shared by all Rolls-Royce workers." He took the title of Lord Hives of Duffield, declaring that: "Possessing no estates or lands, I see no justification for making things difficult by changing my name".

During this period, too, Hives began to make plans for his eventual retirement. This occurred on 11th January, 1957, when Lord Kindersley succeeded him as chairman, with Denning Pearson (later Sir Denning) becoming deputy chairman and managing director.

Ernest Hives who managed the massive Rolls-Royce contribution to the war effort. He joined the company before the first World War as a car tester and rose to become chairman of Rolls-Royce, and Lord Hives of Duffield.

The Avro York airliner and troop transport. The York was a Lancaster bomber with a new fuselage.

The Avro Tudor I. The Tudor was one of the first civil aircraft produced in Britain after the war. It was powered by four Merlins.

The beginnings of civil aviation shortly after the Second World War. Passenger reception tents at Heathrow Airport, London – a mobile post office but permanent telephone boxes and post box.

Before Hives left however, there was much to be done. For although few realised it, the era ahead was to be one of considerable prosperity (although not without its problems), as the world slowly moved out of wartime austerity into a period of recovery.

Rolls-Royce embarked upon many major new civil and military jet-engine developments. Even before the end of the War, the company had been installing Merlin engines in Avro Yorks, a development of the Lancaster bomber, for civil use, and the first such aircraft had flown on 5th July, 1942. The aircraft was used extensively by the RAF, British Overseas Airways Corporation and British South American Airways and other operators, including prodigious feats of flying during the Berlin airlift of 1948. The last Yorks were not phased out of service until the 1960s.

Post-war civil aircraft which used the Merlin

An English Electric Canberra bomber of the Argentine Air Force. The Canberra is powered by two Avon turbojets.

Below: *The Hawker Hunter, powered by the Avon. It was the frontline fighter of the RAF in the years between the Meteor and the Lightning. Hunters were exported to many overseas countries whose flags appear on the nose of this demonstration aircraft. In 1953 the Hunter established a new world air speed record. The picture below left shows Test Pilot Neville Duke with his speed record aircraft.*

The Sud Aviation Caravelle, powered by the Avon, was the first airliner to employ the tail-mounted engine configuration.

BOAC receiving their first two de Havilland Comet 4 aircraft at Heathrow Airport, London. Marks of Comet after the 1 were powered by the Avon.

included the Canadair North Star, and the Avro Tudor and Lancastrian. Clearly, however, the piston-engined airliner was not likely to survive long in the expanding era of the jet engine, and the company was already seriously studying the applications of the gas-turbine to civil aviation.

The opportunity came with the development of the AJ-65, later to be called the Avon, which was really the company's first major departure in gas-turbine engines from the fundamental Whittle concept of centrifugal flow to axial flow, resulting in higher thrust ratings and improved fuel efficiency. The Avon has been described as, "the Merlin of the Jet Age," because it was produced in such large numbers. Going into production initially for the Canberra bomber, the engine was steadily improved through the 1950s, with rising power output, and it has continued in development and production to this day. More than 11,000 military and commercial Avons have been built, powering twelve different types of aircraft, while over 1,000 more have also been built for industrial land-based applications throughout the world, including pumping units for oil and gas pipelines and for electricity generation.

Among the most famous aircraft using the Avon have been the Canberra itself, the Hunter fighter (another classic aeroplane from Sydney Camm, who designed the Hurricane), the supersonic Lightning fighter, the Comet 2 and 4 jet airliners, and the French Caravelle jet airliner (which was the first civil airliner to have its engines at the rear of the fuselage, giving the passengers a smoother, quieter flight).

The Avon has powered the aircraft which have held the world air speed record on three occasions, including the Hawker Hunter flight at 727·6mph (1170·96km/h) on 7th September, 1953, and it was the first engine to achieve a record of over 1,000mph (1609·34km/h), 1,132mph (1821·78km/h) in the Fairey Delta Two aircraft, piloted by Peter Twiss, on 10th March, 1956.

In addition to developing the gas-turbine for pure jet engines, Rolls-Royce at this time also explored its possibilities for driving propellers. As a result the turbo-propeller Dart emerged in 1945, and it eventually entered service in the Vickers Viscount four-engined airliner in 1953. After a slow start, this combination became famous, with over 400 Viscounts sold world-wide, some of which are still in service today.

The Dart is one of the most successful gas-turbine engines ever developed, for it is still in production and in service, not only in Viscounts but also in Dutch Fokker Friendships, the British Aerospace 748 twin-engined feeder-liner, the American Gulfstream I executive transport and several other aircraft.

The Dart was followed by the Tyne turbo-propeller engine in 1955. Initially used in the Vickers Vanguard airliner, it has been a less commercially successful engine. It is still used today in various versions, in such aircraft as the French Breguet Atlantic maritime reconnaissance aircraft, the Short Belfast heavy freighter, the Canadair CL-44 freighter, and the European Transall C-160 military transport and to power warships.

In its continual search for lower fuel consumption, the company also pioneered the world's first "by-pass" or "fan" jet engine to enter service, the Conway. In this type of engine, some of the intake air is passed or "ducted" round the hot parts of the engine and fed back into the hot exhaust gases at the rear. This results in lower jet exhaust velocity, giving increased propulsive efficiency for lower fuel consumption than in "straight through" or "pure" jet engines.

A Dart turbo-prop engine on test in Derby.

A Tyne turbo-prop undergoing anti-icing trials in the nose of a Lincoln bomber seen taking off from Hucknall. The framework ahead of the engine sprayed water into the engine intake and over the propellor to check their resistance to ice forming on them. The picture was taken in summer of 1956.

It is also quieter. The Conway was first proved in military aircraft, but has also been used extensively in civil aeroplanes. These have included the Boeing 707 and Douglas DC-8 jet airliners, the Vickers VC-10 and Super VC-10 rear-engined airliners, and the military Handley Page B-2 Victor bomber and aerial tanker aircraft.

Building on the Conway experience, Rolls-Royce then developed the Spey. Design began in September, 1959, and the first engine ran at the end of December, 1960. This engine has subsequently been highly successful too. Its main uses are in the British Aerospace twin-engined One-Eleven and three-engined Trident series of airliners, and in the Dutch Fokker F-28 twin-engined Fellowship and the Gulfstream II and III executive jets.

The Spey has found substantial military markets, in the Hawker Siddeley Buccaneer combat

A Boeing 707 of BOAC powered by four Conway engines.

A Handley Page Victor tanker trailing its three in-flight refuelling drogues. This tanker can refuel three aircraft simultaneously, and is itself powered by four Conways.

The Nimrod airborne early warning flying radar station, powered by four Speys.

Lord Hives (wearing glasses) discussing the "Flying Bedstead" with the test pilot, Captain Shepherd, who is facing the camera.

aircraft, the Nimrod maritime reconnaissance and airborne early warning aircraft, and the McDonnell Douglas Phantoms for the RAF. It has also recently been chosen for a new Italian combat aircraft, the AMX, and it is now being built under licence in China. There are also plans for future production in Romania and Italy.

The early 1950s also saw dramatic experiments into new applications for the gas-turbine engine, in the field of vertical take-off and landing. At the Farnborough Air Show in 1953, the aeronautical world was electrified by the news that Rolls-Royce had been secretly experimenting in this field, and had flown a device popularly nicknamed "the flying bedstead", because of its appearance, but which in reality was a test rig powered by two Nene engines.

This led to the evolution of various small light-weight direct-lift engines, such as the RB-108 which powered the Short SC-1 vertical take-off and landing research aircraft (with four engines being used for lift and one for propulsion) and the RB162. Work on light-weight lift engines continued for some time. But much of the benefit of the company's work in the vertical and short take-off and landing (V/STOL) field was later vitiated by the cancellation of such major aircraft projects as the Hawker P-1154 vertical take-off fighter and the HS-681 short take-off and landing aircraft in 1965 by the government.

The technology has been kept alive, however, and the current Rolls-Royce emphasis on V/STOL engines is based on the Pegasus used in the Harrier strike fighter. This project itself came into the Rolls-Royce orbit through the acquisition of Bristol Siddeley Engines in 1966.

The 1950s was a trying time for Rolls-Royce. The entire decade, in fact, was filled with pitfalls for the British aerospace industry, as project after project, in both the civil and military fields, fell by the wayside, either cancelled as a result of political decision, or because of lack of civil or military markets, or for other financial or technical reasons.

A major post-war British transport aircraft, the Bristol Brabazon, was cancelled in February, 1952, without ever entering service. The early promise of the world's first jet airliner, the de Havilland Comet, evaporated as a result of the Mediterranean accidents in 1954, which were eventually traced to metal fatigue. But the delays incurred in modifying the aircraft to the eventual Comet 4 powered by Avon engines were such that the aircraft missed the market, and was overtaken in the big jet sales battles of the later 1950s by the Boeing 707 and Douglas DC-8 jets.

Work on another British four-engined jet transport, the military Vickers 1000, using Conway engines, which was also intended to evolve into a civil airliner, the VC-7, for BOAC's Empire and North Atlantic routes, was begun in 1952. But both RAF and BOAC interest waned, and the V-

Opposite: *A new dimension – vertical take-off and landing – was added to aviation by the Rolls-Royce Flying Bedstead which proved the feasibility of jet born vertical lift and control in 1953. The Nene-powered Bedstead is seen with the Short SC1 which employed four RB108 engines for lift and one for propulsion.*

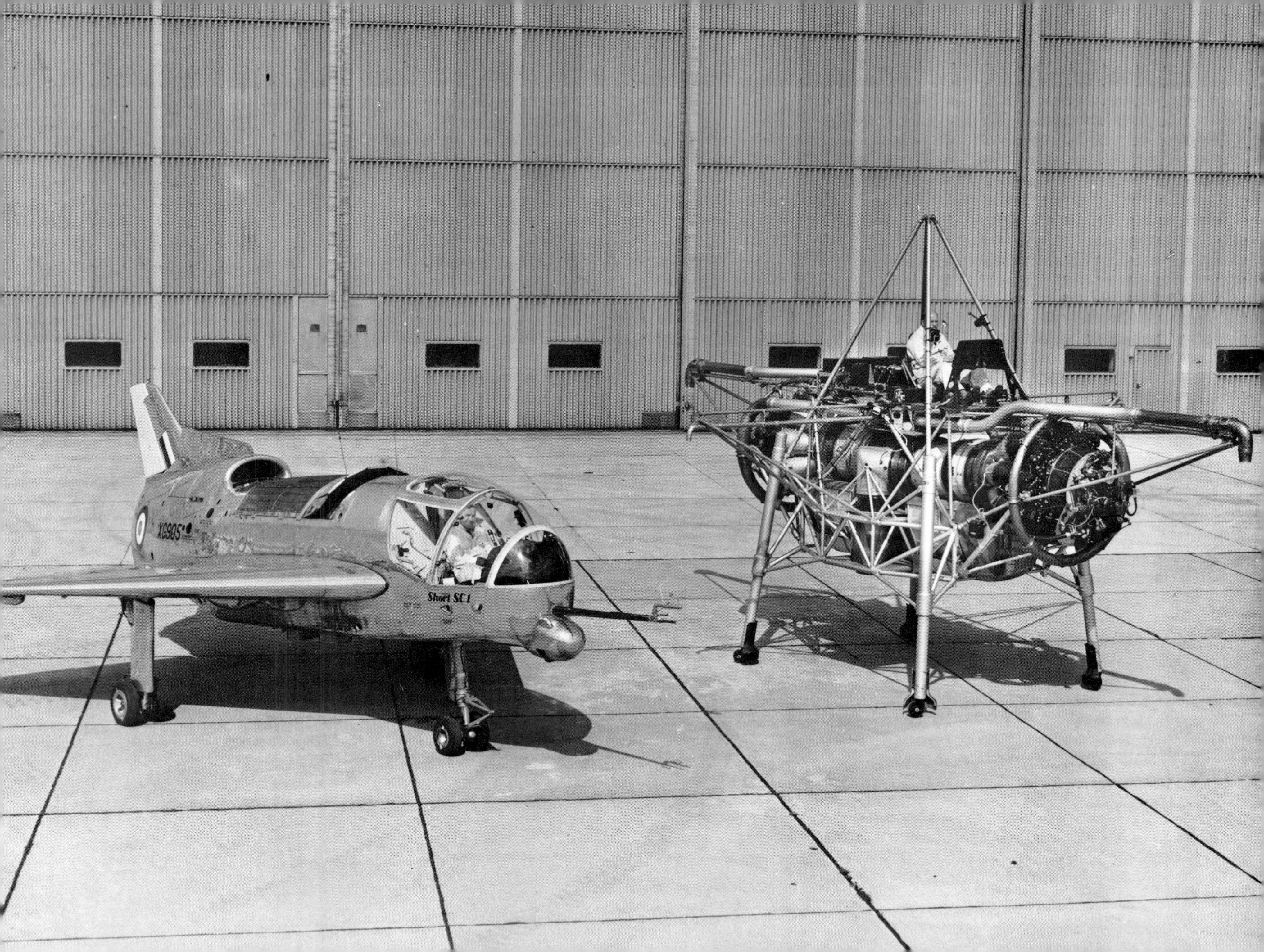
XG905
Short SC.1

The VAK 191B rig. RB108 lift jets were employed to test the control system for the proper aircraft.

The EWR-Sud research aircraft VJ101C-X1 powered by six RB145 engines. Wingtip pods housed two engines each and swivelled. Wingtip engines were reheated in VJ101C-X2.

Opposite: *A Royal Navy Sea Harrier, vertical take-off and landing aircraft, powered by a Pegasus engine.*

250
N

1,000/VC-7 programme was cancelled by the government in November, 1955. Thus, the world's long-range jet airliner market was virtually left open to the Americans – BOAC itself eventually ordered 15 Boeing 707-436 jets in October, 1956.

Britain's other big transport aircraft programme, the turbo-prop Bristol Britannia, also suffered development setbacks, including the loss of the prototype on the mud-flats of the Severn Estuary during a test-flight. This aircraft eventually entered service with BOAC, but it was no match in speed for the American jetliners, and only a small number of Britannias was ever built.

In the short-to-medium haul field, a major domestic battle occurred in the late 1950s, for the development of a new airliner for British European Airways, in which Bristol Aeroplane and Hawker Siddeley combined to offer the Bristol 200 design, in competition with a consortium comprising de Havilland, Saunders-Roe, Fairey and Hunting, which offered the DH-121. This battle was eventually won by the DH-121, using Rolls-Royce RB163 Spey engines. The DH-121 was eventually named the Trident.

There were just as many difficulties in military aviation. The entire aerospace industry was thrown into confusion by the now notorious Defence White Paper of 1957, which placed what many at the time believed to be unnecessarily heavy emphasis on the development of guided missiles at the expense of supersonic combat aircraft. This philosophy led to the cancellation of several aircraft ventures, including the Fairey F-155T, which was based on the record-breaking Fairey Delta Two aircraft. The Avro 730 supersonic bomber, with the Saunders-Roe SR-177 rocket-plus-jet fighter were also cancelled later that year.

It was a situation from which the industry took years to recover. All these problems of the 1950s, however, also brought about a massive and unprecedented round of aircraft company amalgamations that totally reshaped the industry in the late 1950s and early 1960s, mainly at the government's insistence. The industry bowed to this pressure mainly in the hope of better times to come. Those companies which declined to merge, such as Handley Page, found themselves progressively denied new military orders, and turned increasingly to civil ventures, while others went out of aircraft manufacturing altogether, concentrating on aircraft equipment or other engineering activities.

If the decade of the 1950s was traumatic for civil and military aero-engines with many of the new programmes eventually collapsing, the situation for luxury motor cars was just as full of problems. Valuable markets in Europe and the Far East had been lost by the end of the war, and the home market was depressed with the UK's early post-war struggle for survival in a difficult economic period. Clearly there could be no question of allowing such famous names in the motor-car world as Rolls-Royce and Bentley to disappear, and so production was resumed at Crewe, instead of Derby, with the Silver Wraith as the first post-war car of completely new design, closely followed by the Bentley Mark VI. Production also began on the "B" range of petrol engines for the British Army.

Economic conditions improved in the later 1950s, and the rising demand for such models as the Silver Dawn, Silver Cloud, the Bentley T and the continued Phantom series more than justified the original post-war decision to remain in the motor-car field. Rolls-Royce also took the decision in 1957 to reactivate its North American subsidiary, Rolls-Royce Incorporated, as a car sales

In 1957 British government policy elected to develop rocket missiles for defence purposes rather than new generations of manned aircraft. Blue Streak, powered by two RZ-2 rocket motors, is shown at the Spadeadam site in Cumberland just prior to tethered firing.

A Rolls-Royce 1962 Phantom V State Landaulette.

and distribution company in the USA.

The company also decided to build its own coachwork, instead of contracting it out to specialists as in the past. Rolls-Royce had bought Park Ward, specialist coachbuilders in 1938, but in 1959 the London coachbuilding company, H.J. Mulliner, was also acquired.

The growing activity in the motor-car field led the company in 1953 to establish the motor car division as a separate entity at Crewe, although still responsible to the main board of the company at Derby.

Rolls-Royce also took another major decision around this time – to establish oil engine manufacture as an insurance against possible setbacks in the luxury car markets. This new area of endeavour promised strong and expanding export opportunities in road and rail traction and earthmoving machinery. After a period of research and development, it was recognised that ready-made production capacity would be needed, and the Sentinel company at Shewsbury was brought

A Rolls-Royce 1962 Silver Cloud III with coachwork by H.J. Mulliner.

into the now steadily expanding Rolls-Royce group.

The oil engine division was set up in 1956, thus establishing, with the motor car division at Crewe and the aero-engine division at Derby, a "triadic" structure. The company believed at that time that this form of divisional structure was the best for an organisation with a wide range of products with different markets, enabling management to concentrate on specialist tasks and establish closer relationships with world-wide customers.

Another activity initiated at Derby and put into production at Crewe was the American Teledyne Continental Motors' range of light piston aero-engines, geared to the needs of private, club, executive and military aircraft. Although the market was comparatively small then, it grew subsequently and became an important part of the activities of the now separate company, Rolls-Royce Motors Limited but was recently ended by mutual agreement.

6 THE ACQUISITIVE YEARS

During the late 1950s the gas-turbine engine had become much more powerful, larger and more complex, but also more costly to develop. At the same time, the demands of the world's civil and military aviation markets were widening, and competition, especially from the American giants, was becoming fiercer.

A similar situation prevailed in the airframe-manufacturing industry, with too many companies, too many projects, and insufficient cash to go round.

Towards the latter part of the decade, as a result of strong government pressure, the aerospace industry in the UK underwent a transformation. Many of the most famous names that had been in existence since the early part of the century disappeared into massive new groups.

The original Hawker Siddeley Group, formed in 1935, had included such older companies as Sir W.G. Armstrong Whitworth Aircraft, Gloster Aircraft, Hawker Aircraft, A.V. Roe, and Armstrong Siddeley Motors which had all continued to operate under their original names. These were joined in 1959 by Folland Aircraft, and in 1960 the de Havilland and Blackburn groups, to form the new organisation, Hawker Siddeley Aviation (HSA). The various space and guided weapons activities of these companies were also later to be regrouped to form the separate Hawker Siddeley Dynamics (HSD).

Another major new group, the British Aircraft Corporation (BAC), was formed in 1960, comprising Vickers-Armstrongs (Aircraft), English Electric Aviation, the fixed-wing aircraft and missile interests of Bristol Aircraft (formerly the Bristol Aeroplane Company), and Hunting Aircraft.

In yet another regrouping, Westland Aircraft took over the aviation interests of Saunders-Roe in 1959, and the aircraft and helicopter interests of Fairey Aviation in 1960. Also in 1960 Westland acquired the helicopter interests of Bristol Aircraft, to establish Westland Helicopters as the UK's sole helicopter manufacturer. Westland

Aircraft also took over Saunders-Roe's hovercraft activities, and eventually set up the British Hovercraft Corporation.

The aero-engine industry was not immune from this rationalisation. In 1961, Rolls-Royce and English Electric formed Napier Aero-Engines, so that Rolls-Royce could take over the Gazelle engine from the English Electric subsidiary, D. Napier and Son.

Rolls-Royce's main rival at that time, Bristol Siddeley Engines, was itself formed in 1958 by the merger of Bristol Aero-Engines, a subsidiary of Bristol Aircraft, (formerly Bristol Aeroplane Company), and the Hawker Siddeley Group's Armstrong Siddeley Motors. Later, in 1961, BSE also took over the de Havilland engine company and

When Rolls-Royce merged with Bristol, they acquired the Pegasus engine which is the heart of the present-day Harrier. At that time (1966) the aircraft was still in development as the Kestrel, which is shown here.

An early version of the Harrier on a tethered test.

Blackburn Engines from the Hawker Siddeley Group.

Other developments around this time included the formation of Beagle Aircraft in 1962 from the earlier British Executive and General Aviation (which in turn stemmed from the original Auster Aircraft company). Companies which did not become part of the major new groups included Handley Page, Scottish Aviation and Short Brothers & Harland (in which Bristol Aeroplane held at $15\frac{1}{4}$ per cent stake), while another famous manufacturer, Boulton Paul Aircraft, ceased designing its own aircraft in the late 1950s and became part of the Dowty Group in 1961. Britten-Norman (Bembridge), a new light-aircraft builder, was set up in 1964.

In all, no fewer than thirteen major airframe and aero-engine companies were involved in mergers or amalgamations of one kind or another at this time.

With such a strong new organisational structure – HSA, HSD, BAC, Westland, Rolls-Royce and BSE – it seemed in the early 1960s that the aerospace industry as a whole was set for a brighter future. There were many new aircraft and engine programmes either under development or planned, ranging from the Concorde supersonic airliner to the One-Eleven twin-engined airliner and Trident three-engined airliner down to the Beagle light twin-engined executive aircraft.

Outside the industry, it was a decade of rising prosperity in the western world, with air travel in particular on a steep upward curve, indicating an expanding demand for the industry's airliners and engines. By 1960, despite its many difficulties, the UK aerospace industry appeared to be recovering its confidence.

At the Farnborough Air Display in September, 1960, the Society of British Aircraft Constructors (later renamed the Society of British Aerospace Companies) took an optimistic line. Reporting on what it called, "the new shape of the British aircraft industry", it said that since the end of the war, more than £1,000m of its members' products had been exported to some 160 countries and territories overseas, half of which had been achieved in the preceding four years. Of this total, over £300m had come from the sale of aero-engines, of which Rolls-Royce alone had accounted for £138m, supplying twenty-one types of foreign aircraft. Over 1,000 of the 1,617 jet and turbo-prop airliners on order world-wide at that time had or would have British engines, about 63·6 per cent of the total.

Earlier that summer, the new Minister of Aviation had made known the Government's intention of supporting financially the development of four new British airliners, all using Rolls-Royce engines – the Armstrong Whitworth Argosy (four Darts), the de Havilland 121 (later to be named the Trident, using three Speys), and the British Aircraft Corporation VC-10 and Super VC-10 jets (each using four Conways). The news was received with satisfaction by the industry, which had repeatedly stressed to the Government the fact that its competitors abroad already received substantial backing, directly or indirectly, for civil aircraft.

By 1961, the SBAC felt even more optimistic, believing that misunderstandings with the Government were a thing of the past, and that one of the advantages of the recent mergers was that industry and Government had moved closer together, and had developed a deeper understanding of each other's problems.

Mr Edward Bowyer, who was director of the SBAC, said: "This is a development of the great-

The Trident 3 nicknamed the "3½ engined aircraft" since its three Speys were boosted by an RB162 for take-off.

est significance and one which leads to more effective planning of future civil and military aviation requirements, the further development of the home market, effective support of the industry's interests abroad, particularly in Europe, quick decisions and their firm implementation".

The shocks and disappointments, however, lay just around the corner.

In 1960, the Blue Streak rocket (which used Rolls-Royce RZ-2 motors) was cancelled as a weapons system, although it found a secondary use as part of the European ELDO launcher for satellites. In February, 1962, the Conservative Government cancelled support for the Fairey (Westland) Rotodyne vertical take-off airliner (which used two Tyne engines) because of lack of orders, despite earlier interest shown by British European Airways.

In the autumn of 1964, the Labour Government was returned to power after 13 years of Conservative administration. With different ideas about defence policy and spending, it proceeded to cancel some of the industry's most cherished actual and potential programmes.

In the spring of 1965, the British Aircraft Corporation's TSR-2 tactical strike reconnaissance aircraft, one of the industry's biggest

The Jet Provost was the RAF's basic trainer for many years before the recent introduction of the Hawk. The Jet Provost's engines were manufactured by Bristol Siddeley Engines, and so were acquired by Rolls-Royce.

programmes, was eliminated, along with the Hawker Siddeley P-1154 vertical take-off fighter and the HS-681 short take-off and landing aircraft. Even the Concorde had been threatened, but was saved only because of its international nature and tough opposition by the French to any cancellation by the British.

The aerospace industry was stunned, and many believed that it could not survive such a series of devastating blows. Many designers and technicians even quit the industry entirely, many contributing to the "brain drain" abroad which was a feature of the 1960s.

The blow to the engine companies fell on both BSE (whose engines powered the TSR-2 and the P-1154) and Rolls-Royce (which lost the Medway engine in the HS-681). It was to take both the engine and airframe industries several years to recover from the setback these cancellations caused, whilst all the time, foreign competition was intensifying. By 1965, it seemed clear that because of this competition, some further rationalisation was necessary in the aero-engine industry. Even greater resources were likely to be needed, in terms of manpower, money and productive capacity, and in such a situation, any continuation of the intense competition that had emerged between Rolls-Royce and Bristol Siddeley Engines in recent years was no longer tenable. So, in 1966, Rolls-Royce acquired Bristol Siddeley Engines. This provided the necessary resources, including a total combined labour force of over 80,000, for a sustained attack on export markets, and offered a range of engines greater than that of any other engine company in the world.

The merger brought under one management major new civil and military engine programmes. There was the Olympus for military aircraft, such as the Vulcan bombers, and its 593 derivative for the Concorde supersonic airliners, the Proteus turbo-prop engine, the Pegasus vertical take-off engine for the P-1127 V/STOL fighter, and other developments. There were also several smaller engine types, such as the Viper for trainer and target aircraft and for small executive jets and the Orpheus for small military aircraft.

Digesting this merger was a mammoth task for the Rolls-Royce management. At the end of 1967, the Bristol Siddeley operating divisions were incorporated into a revised Rolls-Royce structure. In addition to the motor car and oil engine divisions, and the aero-engine division at Derby, three new divisions came into being.

Firstly, there was the Bristol engine division,

based at Filton and comprising most of the facilities of the former Bristol Aero-Engines. Secondly, the small engine division, based at Leavesden, near Watford, Hertfordshire, and comprising the former de Havilland engine company, was established. Its principal products were in the gas-turbine engine field for helicopters and hovercraft, as well as auxiliary power units. Thirdly, the industrial and marine gas turbine division was set up at Ansty, near Coventry, to bring together the work done over the recent past by both Rolls-Royce and Bristol Siddeley Engines in the field of modified aero-engines for electricity generation, gas pumping, and marine propulsion application.

This last division was also responsible for rocket engines, such as the RZ-2 for the Hawker Siddeley Blue Streak and the Gamma 2 and 8 engines for the Westland Black Arrow satellite launcher (the latter project was also eventually cancelled by the government).

It was during the 1960s also that, again because of the rising cost and complexity of modern gas-turbine engines, and because of the emergence of multi-national airframe programmes, that international collaboration in aero-engine design, development and manufacture became of considerable significance, creating the labyrinth of agreements that pertains to this day.

Rolls-Royce and Bristol Siddeley had both been involved separately in many such ventures. Rolls-Royce had joined forces with Turbomeca of France, for example, in June 1966, setting up Rolls-Royce/Turbomeca to develop and manufacture the Adour engine for the Anglo-French Jaguar jet strike-trainer and other aircraft. Rolls-Royce also collaborated with the Detroit Diesel Allison Division of General Motors in the USA to work on the TF-41 military version of the Spey engine for the Vought A-7 Corsair II aircraft.

The RB199 on full reheat. This military engine powers the advanced Panavia Tornado all-weather combat aircraft.

Bristol Siddeley had been working with SNECMA of France on both the Olympus 593 engine for the Concorde, and on the M-45 turbofan engine for civil and military use (the latter engine being used eventually in the West German VFW-614 twin-jet short-haul airliner).

This concept of international collaboration was progressively refined over the years. The original comparatively simple method of joining with another company on a specific venture evolved gradually into more complex jointly-owned companies.

Thus in 1969 Rolls-Royce became a partner in a new international consortium, Turbo-Union, along with Motoren-und-Turbinen Union of West

Germany and Fiat Aviazione of Italy. The purpose was to undertake what was to become the biggest single military aero-engine development on this side of the Atlantic in peace-time, the RB199 for the new Anglo/West German/Italian Tornado multi-role combat aircraft (MRCA).

As a result of all these domestic and international developments, by 1970 Rolls-Royce had become an international giant, employing nearly 90,000 workers, and with a capital of £65 million, and an annual turnover of more than £300 million of which more than £100 million was in exports – for those days, massive sums indeed.

Up to 1939 Rolls-Royce had been described as: "a sprat, albeit a shining one, in the ocean of engineering". The subsequent thirty years had seen it grow to a position of international, commercial, and technical pre-eminence in engineering in the air and on land, and both on and under the sea (through its post-war work on nuclear submarine power-plants).

The company had suffered its share of all the problems that every big expanding industrial organisation experiences in the course of its history, including war, economic booms and slumps, financial crises, project cancellations, and management changes. Yet, it had weathered them successfully, and by 1970 its name was synonymous world-wide with integrity, reliability and engineering excellence. But although no-one, either inside or outside the company, realised it at the time, the seeds had already been sown for the disaster that was to come so swiftly and engulf Rolls-Royce.

The Tornado in high-speed flight with wings fully swept back and its two RB199 engines in reheat.

Opposite: *A Pegasus engine in a plenum chamber burning (reheat) test pictured on an open-air test-bed at Shoeburyness. The Pegasus is used in vertical take-off aircraft such as the Harrier.*

7 THE RB211

Rolls-Royce began work in the early 1960s on designs for a new "big thrust" engine, as a successor to the Conway. Such a power-plant had become desirable because the company wanted its engines on the new wide-bodied airliners, and in the USA, the company's competitors, General Electric and Pratt & Whitney, had begun developing similar engines. These were intended initially to meet a US Air Force competition for a giant strategic freighter (eventually called the C-5A Galaxy) and later for big new commercial airliners which the major manufacturers, Boeing, Lockheed and Douglas (later part of the McDonnell Douglas Corporation) were all contemplating.

The company believed that the major share of future civil engine business in the 1970s would continue to be in American airframes. Hence, to obtain an adequate number of sales to justify launching a new civil engine, it was necessary to win orders for the engine from at least one major US airframe manufacturer.

Rolls-Royce also believed at that time that if it did not compete, and succeed, in the first round of selection of a big-thrust engine for the new wide-bodied jets, it would be out of the major new civil engine business for at least a decade and probably longer. It would not have been able to participate in the advancing technology, and hence would not have been acceptable to the major airframe constructors both civil and military.

The company needed to keep its stable of civil engines up to date and to meet the anticipated requirements of the airlines. There was also the problem of declining sales of older civil engines. Thus, it was thought vital to get into the "big thrust" engine business quickly.

The company's technical studies were extensive. A design called the RB178 of 25,000lbs (11,340kg) thrust emerged initially, in 1965-66, and work was also begun on a lower-thrust three-shaft engine concept called the Trent.

Rolls-Royce had been invited, as had the

Sir Stanley Hooker, when technical director of Rolls-Royce.

The third RB211-06 during assembly in the pre-rig shop, late in 1968. Early RB211 engines had accessories mounted on the compressor casings. Their location was later changed to the fan casing.

An RB211-06 on test bed in March 1969. The fan blades were made from Hyfil.

Opposite: *Flight testing of the RB211-22 in a VC10 loaned to Hucknall by RAF Support Command* circa *1970.*

other leading engine companies, to quote for a "big thrust" engine by both Boeing and Douglas, which would power a long-range, wide-fuselage airliner for both passenger and freight work. But Rolls-Royce at that time was behind the USA in technology of "high by-pass ratio" engines, because both General Electric and Pratt & Whitney were able to develop their commercial engines from military designs originally financed by the American government for the C-5A programme. Rolls-Royce had no such military advantages for its own big new engine venture, and had to work alone, learning as it went.

The contract for the C-5A power-plant was eventually won by General Electric with the TF-39 engine, predecessor of the present-day CF6 series of "big thrust" engines. Rolls-Royce also lost the competition for a big engine for the new Boeing 747 Jumbo jet airliner, its RB178 being rejected in favour of the Pratt & Whitney JT9D.

A big launching order for the 747 with the JT9D from Pan American World Airways effectively opened the flood-gates for more orders for these giant jets, and began the revolution in "wide-bodied" civil aviation that has continued to this day.

This still left both Lockheed and Douglas, with their own ideas for multi-engined wide-bodied airliners. But while Rolls-Royce continued to work on the RB178, and eventually ran a demonstrator in July, 1966, it had serious mechanical defects and work on it was stopped, although associated rig work continued. Many people in the company believed that had the demonstrator work continued on the RB178, a considerable number of the troubles which beset the eventual RB211 programme might not have occurred.

In addition to the RB178, the company had

G-AXLR
G-AXLR

Mr Dan Haughton (centre) chairman of Lockheed inspecting RB211 work at Derby in December 1971. Willis Hawkins (fifth from left) and Arch Folden (second from left) spent long periods with Rolls-Royce monitoring progress on the engine which was vital to survival of the Lockheed TriStar airliner.

L-1011, the first TriStar to fly.

been preparing a design called the RB207 (initially chosen for the European Airbus) and another, the RB211, and had been actively seeking government financial support for these ventures.

On 23rd June, 1967, Rolls-Royce offered Lockheed the RB211-06, generating 33,260lbs (15,086kg) of thrust. This design incorporated many new technological features, in particular making extensive use of composite materials such as Hyfil. Also, it was a higher-thrust engine than anything Rolls-Royce had done before. The first run was planned for August, 1968.

While work was under way on this engine, the company was involved in long and complex negotiations with Lockheed, seeking an order, and also negotiating with the UK government, for financial support for what was the most expensive civil venture the company had ever undertaken. Total launch costs were then estimated at £91·4m. The thrust of the engine, however, rose steadily, as the airframe manufacturer revised its own ideas of what it needed. By the spring of 1968, the RB211-15 was being offered, with a thrust of 38,000lbs (17,236kg).

During the winter of 1967-68, Rolls-Royce had a big team of top executives, led by Sir David Huddie, the managing director of the aero-engine division at Derby, living in the USA and working closely with Lockheed and Douglas, in its efforts to win a launching order against fierce competition from the American engine companies. It was undoubtedly the most vigorous, sustained and competitive struggle the company had encountered up to that date in civil engine markets.

The efforts, however, were successful. The vital order was won on 29th March, 1968, with orders for 94 Lockheed L-1011 three-engined airliners, later to be called TriStars, from Trans

World Airlines and Eastern Airlines of the USA and Air Holdings, a British aviation financing organisation. Lockheed itself placed an order with Rolls-Royce for 150 "ship-sets" of engines – three engines in each set – for a power-plant called the RB211-22, with an estimated launching cost for the engine alone of some £65·5m. There were also substantial ancilliary costs for such things as special tooling for the programme, which brought the estimated total launch cost to over £100m.

The talks with the government were also successful. On 29th August, 1969, it agreed to provide launching aid of up to 70 per cent of certain costs, retrospective to 1st January, 1967, up to a maximum of £47·13m, with repayment to be made by levies on sales of the engines.

It was a great triumph, proudly acclaimed. Rolls-Royce had broken into the massive American airliner market with a new advanced-technology engine, against the most formidable competition from the two rival US giants, General Electric and Pratt & Whitney. In the spring of 1968, Rolls-Royce believed that it was well on the way to a major new era in civil engine sales, and it pressed ahead with enthusiasm on what was the most challenging technological task it had yet undertaken.

But behind the euphoria of success, the problems were already beginning to emerge.

TriStar aircraft in production in the Lockheed plant, at Palmdale, California. Every TriStar has been powered by RB211 engines.

8 THE COLLAPSE

Opposite: *Reporters interview Mr Dan Haughton, chairman of Lockheed, at Derby (centre) in December 1971. The British press were vitally interested in Lockheed's ability to survive its own financial crisis and so ensure that the TriStar programme and its RB211 engines would succeed. On the left (looking suspiciously at the camera) is Bill Wilson, Lockheed's then vice-president for public relations who made many friends with British air correspondents and worked tirelessly to ensure Lockheed's policies were understood in Britain.*

Throughout 1968 and 1969, as work on the engine progressed, it became increasingly clear that the company had under-estimated the magnitude of the task involved in developing the RB211. The engine design underwent many changes in specification, covering its weight, thrust and noise guarantees. This inevitably meant rising development costs, while the time-scale allowed for its completion began to shorten as Lockheed and the airlines, under the stimulus of intense competition from their rivals, Boeing and Douglas, revised their own plans for the introduction of the RB211 powered L-1011.

Rolls-Royce later admitted that insufficient time had been available to evaluate adequately the effect of the changes needed in all the relevant areas. It admitted that: "Undoubtedly errors of judgement were made, leading to under-estimates of the difficulties and the cost of successfully implementing many of these changes".

It also admitted that: "The realisation of the magnitude of some of the engineering problems consequent upon commitments entered into, and the reaction of taking the necessary steps to deal with them, was either too slow or insufficient. One example of this was the inadequate augmentation of experienced design skills assigned to the RB211 project in time to influence the required redesign of the engine. This redesign led to unforeseen technical problems, including overweight, which led to further cost increases."

The company worked very hard to put these problems right. But the situation began to get out of control during 1970. By that autumn, in a report to the Ministry of Aviation dated 17th September (which remained secret until after the collapse), the company bluntly stated: "We have to report that we have run into severe financial difficulties in the execution of our programme on the RB211 for the Lockheed L-1011 aircraft. The financial implications are such that the board is unable to see how the company can continue in business without the injection of an

additional £40 million of long-term new money over the next two years".

Rolls-Royce remained convinced that in the RB211 the company had a good engine with which to compete in world markets. Nonetheless its estimates of launching costs had risen from £65·5m to £137·5m: "Due to under-estimating difficulties and the cost of satisfactorily solving many of the technical problems involved in this quantum jump forward in technology".

Even at that stage, the possibility of the company's collapse was still not envisaged. After long and tough negotiations, the government agreed on 11th November, 1970, to provide additional launching aid amounting to 70 per cent of the increased costs, up to a maximum of £42 million, with another £8 million coming from the Bank of England. The Midland Bank and Lloyds Bank each provided £5 million.

The government's contribution was subject to an independent audit of the company's affairs, and it also insisted on changes in the top management. Sir Denning Pearson, chairman and chief executive, resigned those posts but remained a non-executive deputy chairman. Lord Cole became chairman.

The government and the new top management team hoped that these changes would correct the problems that had surfaced so formidably. Development of the engine continued, but the team of independent accountants led by Sir Henry Benson had begun its review.

On 22nd January, 1971, the new chairman, Lord Cole, accompanied by Sir Henry Benson, called at the Ministry of Aviation. They reported that in their view, the company was in a most serious situation. The latest assessment of the RB211 showed that the existing development and production programme could not be met. While ultimate technical success was still possible, engine development on the test-bed was largely behind expectations. There would have to be a postponement of initial deliveries for a minimum of six months, and it might well have to be twelve months.

Many modifications to the design were still emerging, at a time when the engine should have been going into full-scale production to meet Lockheed's target of first delivery to full standards in August, 1971. Moreover, these modifications were leading to sharp increases in development and production costs. In view of this, the company considered that only two courses were open to it: either to halt the RB211 (which the board favoured) or to postpone the programme, in the hope that extra time would enable the engineering problems to be overcome – although this would depend upon acceptance of such a situation by Lockheed and its airline customers.

Whichever course was adopted, it was clear that substantial additional cash would be needed, over and above the arrangements already made. For, by late January, it was plain that the estimated launching cost had risen much further. A government study had shown that even if the RB211 were continued, the company would need at least another £150 million to cover its cash-flow deficiencies and potential penalty claims for delays from Lockheed and the airlines of about £45 million to £50 million.

The government was advised that it could not finance Rolls-Royce further without running the risk of becoming legally liable for all the company's debts. In the government's view, it would not be a responsible use of public funds to assume a very large unquantified commitment, either by taking over the company and becoming responsible for its debts and obligations, or by providing money the company had no prospect of repaying.

As a result, the board agreed that the continued development and production of the RB-211 could not be met within the resources either currently available, or likely to become available from additional outside sources.

There appeared to be little option but to stop the RB211 programme, under which circumstances, in view of the heavy compensation that would be claimed by Lockheed and its airline customers, the company would be forced into liquidation. The government's eventual White Paper on the collapse and ultimate rescue operation, published later in January 1972, spelled out the background to this attitude: "The board (of Rolls-Royce) had previously been advised by their lawyers that continuing to trade in circumstances where the company was in effect insolvent would put them at risk under Section 332 of the Companies Act, 1948. Under this section, as it has been interpreted by the Courts, persons who are party to trading by a company at a time when there is no reasonable prospect of its creditors being paid may incur both criminal liability and civil liability for the company's debts, if the company is wound up."

From that point on, events moved swiftly. On 3rd February, the Cabinet under Prime Minister Edward Heath met to consider the situation. The government accepted that a Receiver had to be appointed to protect the interests of debenture holders, but hoped that some arrangements could be made for the RB211 to be continued in some form – perhaps by the government itself introducing legislation to acquire the company's aero-engine business and assets.

By this time, the stories of the imminent collapse had reached the City and Fleet Street, and the newspapers on the evening of 3rd February were full of the imminent disaster.

At 8.45 am on 4th February 1971, the board of Rolls-Royce Limited met again. A statement was agreed to the effect that the loss of resources already committed to the RB211, combined with the losses which would arise on the project's termination, would be such as to exceed the net tangible assets of the company. There was no alternative but to apply for a Receiver to be appointed. Later that day, the trustees for the debenture holders, appointed Mr E. Rupert Nicholson to the post. The company's shares were suspended forthwith on the Stock Exchange.

By a strange irony, on 3rd February, while the last hours of the drama were being played out in London, an RB211 engine had been undergoing tests at Derby, and had been shown to be responding to the modifications, with a thrust of 38,500lbs (17,463kg). The designers and engineers had built an engine that showed signs at last of becoming – as it eventually did – one of the finest aero-engines in the world. However, on the way, its development had bankrupted the company.

9 REORGANISING FOR RECOVERY

The world was stunned. To many people, in all parts of the globe, Rolls-Royce had been synonymous with excellence in engineering, with solidity, reliability and endurance. Overnight, all this had vanished, and the strength of the emotive reaction was as potent a factor in stimulating a rapid rescue and recovery operation as were the financial, technical, industrial and defence implications of the collapse.

Once the Receiver had been appointed, the government moved swiftly. Under the Rolls-Royce (Purchase) Act, 1971, introduced in the spring, the government was authorised to acquire such of the undertaking and assets of the company as were needed to ensure the continuity of national defence, collaborative programmes with foreign countries, and supplies to air forces and airlines as well as private operators world-wide. The government also acquired all the Rolls-Royce patents, to prevent any encroachment on them by foreign parties.

A new government-owned company, Rolls-Royce (1971) Limited, was created to give effect to all these moves, and was registered on 23rd February, 1971. But while the government accepted no liability in respect of the contract between Rolls-Royce and Lockheed, it decided to explore with the Receiver the future of the RB211.

The Receiver was succeeding in holding the company intact, keeping work going wherever he could under the exceptionally difficult and complicated circumstances, to enhance the return to debenture holders by disposing of the business as a going concern. The government appointed a team of "three wise men" – Sir William Cook, Sir St John Elstub and Professor Holder – to undertake an independent assessment of the RB211. On 18th February, 1971, they submitted a report which expressed confidence that the remaining development problems could be overcome, with a six-months' delay in the programme.

Their estimate of remaining launch costs, in

Opposite: *The RB211 certificate of airworthiness was awarded by the British Air Registration Board in February, 1972.*

ENG. Nº
10067

RB211-22B engines during final assembly at the production test facility in Derby.

addition to everything spent to date, was £120 million, including a provision for contingencies. The loss on production was set at £80 million, but such losses, it was thought, might be offset by eventual net profits on spares during the life of the engine, to the value of some £50 million.

It was an encouraging report. Lengthy negotiations with Lockheed and the US government followed during the spring of 1971. These resulted in a new agreement in May, whereby the UK government agreed to finance the continued development of the RB211, provided it could be satisfied that the TriStar itself would go on, and that Lockheed reached with the American government a satisfactory solution to its own serious financial problems.

On 11th May following discussions in London with Lockheed and senior airline representatives, Rolls-Royce (1971) signed a contract with Lockheed to provide the RB211 for the TriStar, but at a much higher price per engine. On 23rd May, Rolls-Royce (1971) formally took over from the Receiver all of the assets and undertaking of the aero-engine and industrial and marine divisions of the old Rolls-Royce Limited (including those assets needed to complete the RB211) together with all rights in the world-renowned Rolls-Royce name and trademarks. On 9th September, the US government guaranteed, with Congressional support, credits for Lockheed, and on 14th September, the new contract between Rolls-Royce (1971) and Lockheed became effective, with airline orders having been confirmed. The way was clear for the RB211 to go ahead. The old Rolls-Royce Limited went into liquidation on 4th October, 1971.

Between the collapse on 4th February and 14th September, when the go-ahead decision was taken, about £40 million more had been spent on the development and initial production of the engine. Full progress had been maintained to protect the contract dates which had been offered to the airlines. At that time, the new company expected that up to £125 million would be needed to complete launching, with a net loss of up to £45 million on the first 555 production engines. In the event the company actually made a profit on those engines.

Thus, the total cost to the government involved in the rescue of the RB211 was about £170 million. This was subsequently revised to between £190 million and £195 million as a result of the US dollar devaluation in late 1971. This

Sir Kenneth Keith, (now Lord Keith) chairman of Rolls-Royce from 1972 to 1980.

reduced Rolls-Royce (1971)'s receipts in sterling from the contracted prices by about £20 million to £25 million.

Everybody breathed a sigh of relief – except for the creditors and shareholders of the old company who were the most likely to suffer, and who at that time had no means of knowing what they would eventually receive in compensation for the collapse.

The RB211, however, had been saved and the nation's aero-defence needs safeguarded. Rolls-Royce was back in business, across a wide spectrum of aero-engine and industrial, marine and nuclear powerplant activities.

The old company's motor-car division, diesel engine division and the department making small, light piston engines for aircraft, had not been acquired by the government, however. They remained in the hands of the Receiver, until he floated them off on the Stock Exchange as an entirely separate new company, Rolls-Royce Motors Limited.

Since the collapse Rolls-Royce (1971), which changed its name back to Rolls-Royce Limited in 1977, has not engaged in motor-car manufacture. But the separate company, Rolls-Royce Motors, has moved on to resounding successes in world markets, and Rolls-Royce cars remain as famous and reliable today as ever, both at home and throughout the world. In 1980 Rolls-Royce Motors merged with Vickers Limited, but is still heavily engaged in motor-car manufacture for home and export.

The government's White Paper on the rescue operation, explained why events had progressed as they did. "The failure of the old Rolls-Royce company", it declared, "had confronted the government with a situation of immense gravity, affecting not only our own armed forces and national airlines, but many overseas governments and airlines as well. Our reputation as a trading nation and as leaders in technology would have been damaged if the government had not stepped in quickly and effectively to preserve the physical resources of the company and to provide finance and leadership for continuing on a new basis.

"Something of the order of 100,000 jobs would have been at stake at Rolls-Royce and their suppliers, of which around a quarter was attributable to the RB211 project, with contingent risks in respect of economic and social costs; if uncertainty had been prolonged, the solvency of many major firms would have been at risk and business confidence would have been gravely impaired throughout the country".

In effect, the government was pointing out how deeply the activities of a big company like Rolls-Royce weave their way into the economic, industrial and social fabric of the nation, something which is true even to this day.

The rescue of the RB211 had involved over eight months of intensive effort and decisions of "utmost difficulty" on both sides of the Atlantic. The British government itself wrote the closing words to the company's most traumatic period from February, 1971 to January, 1972, in the White Paper, when it declared its belief that: "A stable basis has now been provided for continuing the vital aero-engine business of Rolls-Royce, and for preserving their high technical reputation. They (the government) look to the management and workers of Rolls-Royce (1971) Limited to complete the task successfully, and thus enable the company to retain its place, in collaboration with industrial partners in this and other countries, as a major supplier of civil aero-engines to world airlines".

Opposite: *Mid-1978 saw the completion of the 555th RB211-22B.*

555th
PRODUCTION
RB211-22B

10 POWER FOR THE WORLD'S AIRLINES

One of the TriStar's three stars, an RB211 on the starboard wing.

A significant step forward in the recovery of Rolls-Royce (1971) occurred on 5th October, 1972, when Sir Kenneth (later Lord) Keith, the banker who was chairman of Hill, Samuel & Company, was appointed chairman of the company. He succeeded Lord Cole, who had borne the heavy burden of nursing the new company through its early stages. Now, a new era was about to begin, in which the company recovered its confidence, grew steadily in stature, and expanded massively in world markets.

Sir Kenneth had been associated with aviation for some time, as deputy chairman of British European Airways from 1965 (which post he relinquished on joining Rolls-Royce). Prominent in the City of London, and director of several major companies, Sir Kenneth quickly proved himself to be one of the most energetic and successful individual salesman the company had ever had. He was the driving force behind the revival of the company's fortunes during the 1970s. He continued the policy of ensuring that Rolls-Royce captured as big a share as possible of the burgeoning world markets for civil aero-engines, whilst also securing a sizeable stake for the long-term future in the military engine field.

It was apparent that the world's major airlines would have to re-equip their fleets through the later 1970s and the early 1980s. This requirement would be due partly to the rising volume of traffic and the increasing age of aircraft already in service, but also because of mounting pressures from soaring fuel costs and environmental difficulties, which would call for a new generation of engines of much improved fuel efficiency and lower noise levels. These new fleets would be needed to carry the airlines through to the end of this century and even beyond. They would also provide a rare opportunity for Rolls-Royce to accumulate a massive volume of new engine orders on which to sustain itself and grow through the years ahead.

This belief proved well founded. Since 1st January, 1978, well over 2,500 new airliners of all

ROLLS
RR

The RB211-524 installation on a Boeing 747 aircraft is checked by service engineers.

RB211-524 engines for Pan Am's TriStar 500 aircraft.

kinds have been ordered or optioned throughout the world, as part of a re-equipment tide that is expected eventually to add more than 3,500 new airliners, worth more than £50 billions, to the world's air transport fleets by the mid-1980s. Of this, Rolls-Royce has already captured considerable business with the family of RB211 engines already under way. The company hopes to do even better in the years to come with new programmes now in the development stage.

The company's strategy in the civil field over the next few years is based on investing substantial sums on the development of these various civil engine programmes. The major concentration is the continued development of the RB211 family of engines in all versions, to meet increasing demand for such airliners as Boeing 747 Jumbo jets, Lockheed TriStars, and the new Boeing 757 short-to-medium range twin-engined jet airliner. In the two former aircraft, Rolls-Royce has already firmly established itself with the "big thrust" versions of the RB211. These range between the 42,000lbs (19,050kg) thrust of the Dash 22 model up to the 55,000-56,000lbs (24,948-25,400kg) thrust of the Dash 524G, the latest and most powerful RB211 model, and there

The first run of the RB211-535 for the Boeing 757 airliner. Engineers and technicians await the important moment.

is further potential to carry the engine to higher powers if required in the future for even bigger versions of the 747 and TriStar.

When the Boeing 757 jet airliner was being developed, Rolls-Royce won the coveted position of "launch engine supplier", with the Dash 535 version of the RB211 of 37,400lbs (16,964kg) thrust, with orders from British Airways and the American company, Eastern Airlines. Yet another variant of the RB211 is under consideration for the European Airbus.

Thus, in less than a decade after the collapse, the RB211 has consistently proved to be one of the world's most fuel-efficient and reliable aero-engines, entering service with an increasing number of airlines first in the Lockheed TriStar and later in the Boeing 747, and winning new orders against some of the most formidable competition from its American rivals. The engine

RB211-535 engines power the new Boeing 757, here shown in model form.

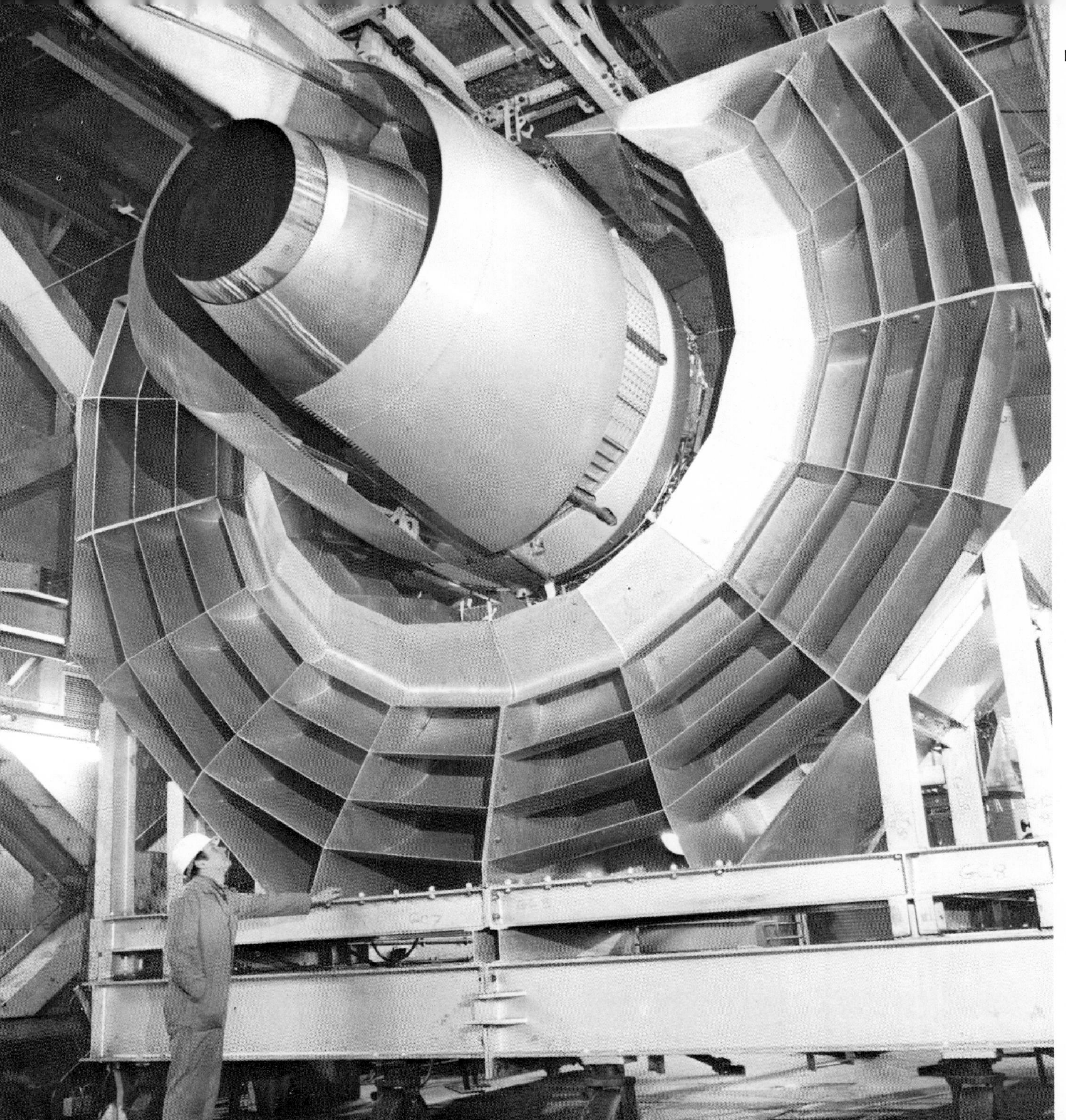

RB211-535 thrust reverser testing at Derby.

A Saudia TriStar takes off from Jeddah.

The majority of Hawker Siddeley (now British Aerospace) HS125 executive jets are powered by two Viper turbojets.

has now begun to widen its sphere of influence into other types of aircraft.

Through the 1980s and beyond to the end of this century, the RB211 in all its versions will remain one of the major contributors to the company's success in world civil aero-engine markets. It more than vindicates the original decision in the early 1960s to commit the company to its development, and the government's decision in 1971 to rescue the company and continue with the engine. For it is now abundantly clear that, had Rolls-Royce and the government decided differently, the company – and the nation itself – would by now have been out of the "big engine" market, at a time when the world air transport industry is expanding at a rapid rate, creating an unprecedented demand for aero-engines as well as for new civil airframes.

This expansion is not confined to the large airliners and largest engines, but is in many areas either already taking place, or is expected to do so, in the smaller aircraft.

The "big thrust" market is generally understood to mean "wide-bodied" aeroplanes, seating between 200 and 400 passengers, such as Boeing 747s and the semi-wide-bodied 767s, Lockheed TriStars and McDonnell Douglas DC-10s and European A-300 Airbuses. These aircraft are proving popular with airlines and passengers, and are selling well.

Underneath them in size there is another large market, for airliners seating between 100 passengers to 200. In this vast field there are already such familiar airliners as the British Aerospace Tridents and One-Elevens, and the American Boeing 737, 727 and McDonnell Douglas DC-9 short-to-medium range jet airliners.

In many cases, these aircraft are ageing and becoming less fuel-efficient, and will need to be replaced through the coming decade, creating a new demand for engines in the 20,000lbs-plus (9,072kg) thrust class, to replace those engines which have been in service for many years, such as Spey turbo-fans.

Furthermore, in the aircraft size category below 100 seats, there is another big market waiting to be exploited. These are the so-called "commuter" or "feeder-liner" aircraft. Neither should we forget the smaller aircraft, the "business" or "executive" jets – all in turn requiring new, quieter, fuel-efficient power-plants.

Thus, apart from what the company is doing, with the RB211, there are vast opportunities for other new classes of engine to fill all these expanding needs. Rolls-Royce is well aware of these opportunities. Some time ago, it began work as a private venture on a new type of engine, the RB401, at about 5,500lbs (2,495kg) thrust, intended as a successor to the Viper and Orpheus, for business and executive transports and light military aircraft. The development

A Boeing 747 of British Airways powered by four RB211-524 fanjets.

Rollout of the Gulfstream American Gulfstream III long range executive jet, powered by two Spey turbofans. The Gulfstream I is powered by two Rolls-Royce Dart turboprops and the Gulfstream II by two Speys.

Bahamasair
C6-BED

programme proved very successful and work is continuing, with a view towards eventual production of an engine meeting in-service needs of small-aircraft users around the mid-1980s. From the successful work on the RB401 there also emerged in the late 1970s a larger, new-generation engine, the RB432 turbo-fan, in the 18,000–20,000lbs (8160–9,070kg) thrust class, with potential for growth beyond that level, so that it would be capable of meeting requirements for aircraft up to about 140-150 seats – in other words, the replacements for the ageing Tridents, One-Elevens, boeing 727s, 737s and DC-9s.

Because of the cost and complexity of such new engines, however, even a company of the size of Rolls-Royce, with all its financial and technical capabilities, cannot now contemplate the development of such a power-plant alone, bearing in mind all the other demands, civil and military, on its resources. For this reason, and because of the intense competition that exists in the world aero-engine market today, international collaboration has become almost a *sine qua non* of both civil and military engine development. Thus, Rolls-Royce began in the late 1970s to consider such collaboration and looked around the world for partners.

Following extensive negotiations, in late 1979 the company signed an agreement with the three major Japanese engine companies –

A British Aerospace One-Eleven powered by two Rolls-Royce Spey turbofans.

Opposite: *A British Aerospace 748 airliner is powered by the Dart turboprop.*

The power unit of Concorde, the Olympus 593 turbojet.

Ishikawajima Harima Heavy Industries, Kawasaki Heavy Industries and Mitsubishi Heavy Industries – for the joint development of a 20,000lbs plus (9,070kg) thrust aero-engine partly based on the RB432 and called the RJ500. A special joint company, Rolls-Royce and Japanese Aero-Engines, was set up in 1980 to undertake this work.

The RJ500 design is for a quiet, reliable turbo-fan engine for future short-to-medium range airliners seating between 120 and 160 passengers. The joint company's aim is to have the detailed design of the engine complete in time to fit the future needs of the aircraft manufacturers. A decision on whether to press ahead with full-scale development will depend on how the market develops. Potential customers include Boeing for new versions of the 737 short-haul airliner, Airbus Industrie of Western Europe for a new series of "Single Aisle" narrow-bodied jets, and Fokker of Holland who are planning the F29 twin-jet. Work on the RJ500 is being done by a

Opposite: *British Airways Concorde supersonic airliner. powered by four Olympus 593 engines, over St. Michael's Mount in Cornwall.*

British airways
G-BOAA
G-BOAA

A Fokker F28 Fellowship powered by two Spey turbofans.

joint team from three Japanese companies and from Rolls-Royce working together. If the market decrees that the engine does go ahead, it could well be in demand among the world's airlines for the next thirty years.

Whilst committing substantial resources to both the RB211 family and the RJ500, Rolls-Royce continues to work on its other civil engines, including both the Spey turbo-fan and the Dart turbo-propeller engine. These are still in production – after some thirty years in the case of the Dart. Both these engines are in fact classic examples of the massive continuing profitable business that can accrue over long periods of time for successful power-plants. Sometimes they can repay their initial investments many times over. They illustrate very clearly the validity of the fundamental principle that led the company to embark upon the RB211 itself in the early 1960s, and which impelled the government to continue with the engine in 1971. This is that despite heavy initial outlays, the rewards for successful products in the world aero-engine markets can not only be immense, but can be sustained for very considerable periods of time.

Quite apart from the technological "spin off" that can accrue from working at the expanding frontiers of advanced technology, aero-engine development can be a very rewarding activity financially, provided the initial investors are prepared to wait long enough for their investment to mature. This fact is also demonstrated by the cash returns from sales of spares by the company on its civil and military engines over recent years. In the five years from 1975 to 1979 inclusive, Rolls-Royce sold world-wide no less than £1,025 million-worth of new civil and military aero-engines, whilst at the same time selling another £1,000 million of spares. The company undertook another £968 million of repairs, overhauls and refurbishing work – a total of nearly £3,000 million of aero-engine business alone. Of this, very nearly half has been for export.

Through the 1970s, Sir Kenneth Keith and his team were thus able to sustain a continued high inflow of new orders for the company, and this has been maintained into the early 1980s. Thus, a very high workload now confronts the company.

Rolls-Royce's name and reputation is at stake on these contracts, for upon the ability of Rolls-Royce to produce its engines at the right time, at the right price and up to the required specification will depend whether or not old customers come back again and new ones enter

The Rolls-Royce stand at the 1980 Farnborough Air Show. Left to right: an RB211-535, a full-size model of the RJ500, and an RB211-524.

the fold. Once delivered, the company must also help its customers to maintain their engines in service for a very long period of time. Thus, the company devotes a substantial and growing amount of time and effort to sustaining a high level of after-sales service in the field world-wide.

Late in 1979, Sir Kenneth Keith let it be known that he was ready to retire. He had carried the company forward for eight years, during which time he had on occasion spent as much as seven months of the year travelling abroad on the company's business, especially seeking out the big civil and military contracts which have done so much to help restore the company's prestige world-wide. He formally left the company on January 22, 1980, with a life peerage in recognition of his efforts. He took the title of Lord Keith of Castleacre.

His successor, and the current chairman of the company, is Lord McFadzean of Kelvinside – again no stranger to the aviation business, for he was for a time the chairman of British Airways, after his retirement as chairman of Shell Transport & Trading. It is Lord McFadzean's task to take the order book generated over the past few years and turn it into the engines the world's airlines want – a formidable task that will involve, for example, about trebling of production of the RB211 engine alone in the period between 1979 and 1982, whilst continuing the development and production of other civil and military powerplants.

11 SERVING THE MILITARY MARKET

Opposite: *The interceptor version of the Tornado with air to air missiles under the fuselage, and RB199 engines in full reheat.*

The market for military aero-engines is also expected to expand considerably over the next few years, notwithstanding political pressures for disarmament. Many countries, especially in the North Atlantic Treaty Organisation and throughout the Third World, are updating and expanding their existing air forces or embarking upon the development of air power.

Rolls-Royce has been closely involved in the military aero-engine market ever since Royce designed his first military engine, the Eagle, at the start of the First World War, and sales of military engines now account for a substantial proportion of the company's overall turnover – £488 million in 1979, for example. The company is thus in a strong position to meet the growing needs of world air forces for engines for combat aircraft of all kinds. Rolls-Royce is the major supplier of aero-engines and other power-plants for the UK defence programme and the RAF. It is also the major supplier for overseas markets, either in airframes built in the UK for direct export, or through engines sent overseas or built overseas under licence, for installation in foreign-built airframes.

This international pattern of collaborative design, development and manufacture of military aero-engines has already gone much further than in the civil engine field. It is likely to expand further during the 1980s, as costs continue to rise, and the technological demands upon the aero-engine manufacturers increase. A third factor influencing the likely growth of collaborative agreements will be the increasing desire of the North Atlantic Treaty Organisation for greater standardisation of advanced weapons systems – a desire that has already manifested itself in a number of other programmes, such as small arms and anti-tank weapons, for example.

Nowhere is this international collaboration better illustrated than in the RB199 turbo-fan engine for the international Panavia Tornado all-weather combat aircraft. This represents the biggest single collaborative military engine pro-

A *Japanese Mitsubishi F-1 single seat close support fighter powered by two Adour engines, built in Japan under licence.*

Below: *Breguet Atlantic maritime reconnaissance aircraft powered by two Tyne propjets. This aircraft was built as a collaborative programme between France, Germany, Italy and the Netherlands and its engines by Belgium, France and Germany. The same engines were used in the Franco-German Transall military transport.*

gramme on which Rolls-Royce has been involved in peace-time. It is expected ultimately to yield well over 2,000 engines for the 800-plus Tornado aircraft that are projected. There is also a good prospect that in the long-term there will be substantial exports of the RB199, and that it will evolve into a family of derivative engines in the same way that on the civil side, the RB211 has become a family of power-plants for a widening variety of airliners.

The RB199 has been designed, developed and is now being manufactured by the international tripartite consortium called Turbo-Union, in which Rolls-Royce is partnered by Motoren-und-Turbinen Union of West Germany and Fiat Aviazione of Italy. The engine is at present supplied solely for the Tornado programme, which is being undertaken by Panavia, itself an international tripartite consortium in which British Aerospace is partnered by Messerschmitt-Bölkow-Blohm of West Germany and Aeritalia of Italy.

Trials of the radar for the Nimrod airborne early warning (AEW) aircraft were carried out in a modified Comet powered by four Rolls-Royce Avons.

A British Aerospace Lightning Mark 6 all-weather fighter powered by two Avon engines.

A derivative of the RB199 is also being considered at the moment, as the potential powerplant for another major new combat aircraft programme now under study in Western Europe. This would be a new tactical fighter to replace the ageing Jaguar in the RAF and French Air Force and the Phantoms in the West German Luftwaffe. At the time of writing, no decision has been taken on development. But the company has high hopes that through Turbo-Union, or perhaps even some wider organisation that may include French aero-engine partners, it will have a major share in this next major military aero-engine programme on this side of the Atlantic. However, here, as in the civil field, competition from the United States manufacturers could be fierce.

The RB199 is a particularly good example of the way in which the rapidly advancing technology of aerial warfare has dictated a constant reappraisal of military engine technology. The needs today range across the entire spectrum of

speeds and payloads, from comparatively slow-speed "loitering" capability to that of high-speed, high-power, "climb-to-altitude". The Tornado aircraft meets all these operational needs, and it can sustain long distance flights out to sea, to detect and destroy enemy aircraft seeking to attack the UK and the Western European seaboard via the "back door". At the same time, however, the Tornado must be capable of tremendous speed, to carry it up to the great heights where it must locate and eliminate enemy aircraft. Yet another requirement is for low-level but high-speed "interdiction" – the penetration of enemy defences behind the battle lines.

This combination of performances places severe technological demands on the skills of the engine designers. In one power-plant, they must build in economy of fuel consumption, the ability to move from slow speed to very high speed in a few seconds, and a sustained running power to enable the aircraft to stay aloft for long periods of time, as well as to achieve its climb-to-height and supersonic low-level dashes when required. It is widely accepted that in the RB199 the designers have achieved this combination of performances. The engine is already being rated as one of the finest military aero-engines yet developed, and one in which a number of foreign countries have begun to show interest. Like the RB211 on the civil side, it is likely to be one of the mainstays of the company's aero-engine activities for many years to come.

The other major military aero-engines on which the company's present position is based include the Pegasus for the Harrier vertical take-off fighter (and also the more recent maritime version, the Sea Harrier), which is already in service with the RAF and the US Marine Corps and the Spanish Navy. An advanced version of the Pegasus is under development to meet the requirements of the advanced AV-8B version of the Harrier, which may be built in the USA for both the US Marine Corps and the US Navy.

The Adour turbo-fan engine is another example of international collaboration at work in military aero-engine development. It was initially developed in the mid to late 1960s in conjunction with the French Turbomeca company, for the Anglo-French Sepecat Jaguar jet strike-trainer aircraft. The Adour engine has subsequently been

The McDonnell Douglas AV-8B prototypeV/STOL fighter, a derivative of the Harrier powered by the Pegasus vectored thrust turbofan. This has been developed by the American company under licence from British Aerospace.

Opposite: *The Panavia Tornado multi-role combat aircraft powered by two reheated RB199 turbofans.*

Building the Pegasus vectored thrust turbofan at Bristol.

used in a number of other highly successful military aircraft, the Hawk trainer and light combat aircraft for the RAF and several foreign air forces, and the Japanese Self Defence Force's Mitsubishi T-2 trainer and F-1 fighter support combat aircraft, with engines for the two latter aircraft being manufactured under licence in Japan by Ishikawajima Harima Heavy Industries. The engine is also expected to be manufactured under licence in India for the Jaguar combat aircraft for the Indian Air Force. And the Adour is now on offer in the Hawk for the US Navy's competition for a new advanced jet trainer aircraft, designated the VTX.

Rolls-Royce is also still involved with the Spey to meet the demands of the RAF's Phantom fighter force. The Spey has also been selected by the Italian government for use in a new combat

A British Aerospace Hawk trainer powered by one Adour turbofan in the livery of the RAF's famous Red Arrows aerobatic team.

A Jaguar fighter of the Muscat Air Force. The Jaguar is powered by two Adour engines.

The Adour turbofan on test with reheat lit.

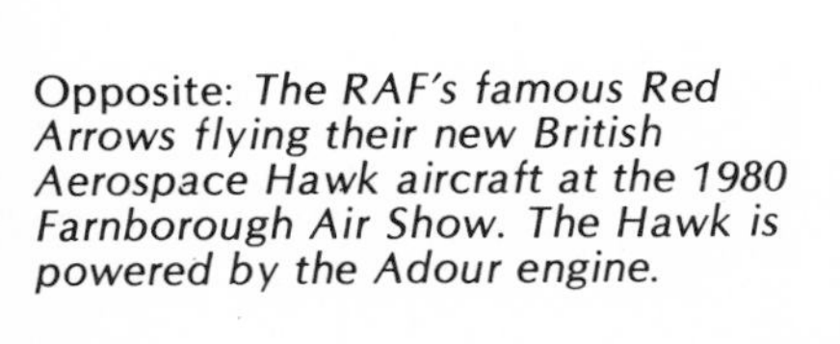

Opposite: *The RAF's famous Red Arrows flying their new British Aerospace Hawk aircraft at the 1980 Farnborough Air Show. The Hawk is powered by the Adour engine.*

aircraft, the AMX and it has been manufactured under licence in China for some time. More than 4,700 Spey turbo-fan civil and military engines have been ordered, to power nine different types of civil and military aircraft. It is estimated that, with the Italian combat aircraft alone, the Spey is likely to continue in manufacture for the best part of the next twenty years. Another version of the engine is the TF-41, which is developed and produced jointly with the Detroit Diesel Allison Division of General Motors for the US Air Force and US Navy's Vought A-7D and A7-E Corsair II fighter and ground attack aircraft.

The Viper family of small civil and military jet engines is also still running strongly, with the latest development being the Viper 632, designed specifically for use as a military engine in the trainer and light attack role, rated at 4,000lbs (1,814kg) thrust. The Viper 632 powers such aircraft as the Italian Macchi MB-339 trainer and the MB-326K. Other versions of the Viper are in production and will power the Yugoslav/Romanian ORAO twin-engined strike aircraft, the Yugoslav Soko Galeb and Jastreb aircraft, and the Indian Air Force's HJT-16 Kiran. In all some twenty-nine air forces fly Viper-powered

A British Aerospace Nimrod maritime reconnaissance aircraft, powered by four Spey turbofans.

The Macchi MB339 powered by one Viper turbo-jet.

aircraft throughout the world, and well over 4,000 of these engines have been built. Vipers are now used in forty-one countries.

Rolls-Royce is also involved in the development and production of missile motors, and its Odin ram-jet powers the British Aerospace Sea Dart anti-aircraft and anti-missile guided missile for the Royal Navy for use in small warships.

Finally, Rolls-Royce has also played for years a major role in the field of small gas-turbine engines for helicopters, through its factory at Leavesden in Hertfordshire.

The Gnome turbo-shaft engine is still in production after more than 1,800 engines have been delivered. After eighteen years of service, this engine has now accumulated over three million flying hours of helicopter experience. There are twenty-one civil and military operators worldwide currently using Gnome-powered helicopters in a variety of land and ship-based roles.

Oil rig support and rescue, anti-tank and anti-submarine warfare, military tactical assault and replenishment, disaster relief, civil contract hire and VIP transport are among the many roles performed by the ubiquitous helicopters

A Sea King helicopter of the RAF search and rescue service. Sea Kings are powered by two Gnome turbo-shaft engines.

A Westland Lynx in hiding waiting to fire off its eight guided missiles. The Lynx is powered by two Gem turboshaft engines.

Opposite: *Britain's only twin-rotor helicopter, the Belvedere, flying at Hucknall.*

powered by this versatile engine. The power output of the Gnome has increased progressively over the years, and among aircraft currently using it are the Westland Sea King and Commando helicopters. Deliveries of the engine are programmed through 1981, and further new sales prospects are being pursued that should keep the engine in production for the rest of this decade.

In addition to the Gnome, the Gem turboshaft engine has also generated a substantial volume of orders, especially for the highly successful twin-engined Westland Lynx helicopter. This is one of the three helicopters developed under the long-standing Anglo-French programme that also produced the Gazelle light helicopter and the Puma tactical transport helicopter. The Gem-2 engine is now in service in Lynx helicopters with the Royal Navy, British Army, Royal Netherlands Navy and the French Navy, while other customers include Norway, Brazil, Argentina, Qatar and Denmark. A later variant, the Gem-4 engine, is in service with the Royal Netherlands Navy.

Also under the Anglo-French helicopter programme mentioned above, Rolls-Royce participated with Turbomeca in the production of the Astazou III engine for the Gazelle light helicopter. Over 400 engines have been supplied for this helicopter, now in service with the British and French forces. Another 200 engine sets have been supplied to Turbomeca for aircraft for the French forces. This engine programme is now complete, but there is the possibility of further requirements for both the British and French governments, and an engine overhaul programme is currently in progress at Leavesden.

For the future, the British, Italian, French and West German helicopter manufacturers are studying plans for a new generation of helicopters to meet the needs of the NATO nations until the end of this century. In these discussions, the helicopter-engine manufacturers, including Rolls-Royce, have been closely consulted, and it is expected that a new generation of helicopter engines will emerge in the 1980s. To meet this requirement Rolls-Royce itself has a new helicopter-engine design under way.

XG452

12 POWER ON LAND AND SEA

Opposite: *The SR-N5 hovercraft is powered by one Gnome engine.*

The use of gas turbines derived from aero-engines in both industrial and marine applications is now a growing part of the overall business of Rolls-Royce. The relatively compact, light-weight nature of even the biggest gas-turbine engines developed for aviation use, and their high degree of reliability, makes them ideally suitable for unmanned gas and oil pumping stations, for electrical power generation, for use on off-shore oil and gas development and production rigs, and as ship-propulsion units. These engines are capable of producing substantial outputs of power quickly, cleanly and economically whilst occupying only limited space, and requiring the minimum of maintenance and overhaul once installed.

It is not surprising, therefore, that exploitation of the spin-off into industrial and marine applications that the gas-turbine engine can provide has become a major contributory factor to the overall growth of Rolls-Royce. In the five years from 1975 to 1979, sales of the company's industrial and marine equipment have amounted to no less than £543 millions, and this activity is expanding every year.

This activity is based at Ansty, near Coventry, where all these applications have been pioneered since 1959. Since then, sales of well over 2,000 engines for non-aviation uses have been achieved, of which sixty-five per cent have been for export, to operators in over fifty countries.

Complete installations of aero-derived gas-turbine power can be undertaken in the widest variety of roles, across a wide spectrum of industries and in the greatest possible range of climactic and terrain conditions, from the deserts of the Middle East to the jungles of South-East Asia and the Arctic snow and ice. So far, the company has never failed to meet the most exacting demands, imposed by its customers.

Probably the most significant of all these new uses for gas-turbine power is that of marine propulsion. Gas turbines have revolutionised the

SRN5
SR N5

The SR-N4 cross-Channel hovercraft The Princess Anne *has four Proteus engines.*

design and lay-out of warship machinery, and have led to a radical rethinking of overall warship design.

Four of the company's basic aero-engines have been adapted for maritime use.

The Gnome turbo-shaft engine of 1,440bhp is primarily a power unit for the SR-N5 and SR-N6 range of hovercraft air-riding vehicles built by the British Hovercraft Corporation.

The Proteus turbo-propeller engine has also been adapted for hovercraft, giving between 4,500 and 6,000bhp. It is used in the big SR-N4 hovercraft operated by British Rail Seaspeed and Hoverlloyd which run across the English Channel carrying passengers and vehicles. It is additionally employed in a wide range of fast patrol boats, gun-boats and training vessels. Over 270 Proteus marine engines have been sold to date, and operating experience with this engine at sea now amounts to some 600,000 hours.

The Tyne, also orginally developed as a turbo-propeller engine, with 5,340-6,000bhp, is used in hydrofoils for the US Navy, and in frigates and destroyers of the Royal Navy and other world navies.

Finally, the Olympus marine engine has been derived from the basic power-plant which was used in the V-bombers and later also adapted as the Olympus 593 for the Concorde supersonic airliner. With its massive output of between 28,000 and 29,600bhp, it is extensively used in frigates, destroyers and even larger vessels, such as the Royal Navy's latest class of 16,000 tons (16,250 tonnes) anti-submarine cruisers – *HMS Invincible*, which has already joined the fleet, and *HMS Illustrious* and *Ark Royal*, now under construction. Eighty marine Olympus engines have been installed in the major warships of fifteen navies, and 180 have been ordered, of which many are for export.

In addition to these engines, the company is also developing the SM-1A intermediate power engine, of 17,100bhp, for application in a wide variety of craft. This is derived from the RB168-66 engine used by the American Air Force and Navy, and is intended to be equally suitable for both main propulsion and for cruise-speed requirements, in such vessels as destroyers, frigates and corvettes. The SM-2B of 17,100bhp is a variant with a light-weight mounting system especially

The engine room of the Royal Swedish Navy's Spica fast patrol boat, with its three Proteus engines.

designed for smaller, faster vessels such as hydrofoils, hovercraft, fast attack craft and corvettes.

There are now so many various combinations of these power-units, that it is possible to power virtually any kind of marine craft, a measure of flexiblity that has already resulted in no less than twenty-six of the world's navies specifying Rolls-Royce marine engines.

A version of the RB211 engine itself is being developed, for use in large merchant ships, such as liquid natural-gas carriers or big ice-breakers, where the power-unit can be mounted high in the after-superstructure. Another use is on off-shore oil and gas platforms. The RB211 unit is incorporated in a self-contained generating package, suitable for installation on a wide range of ships and rigs.

In addition to the maritime roles of these aero-derived gas-turbine engines, however, the company has been active in exploiting the land-sited industrial possibilities. This business is based substantially on the highly successful

The Royal Navy anti-submarine cruiser, HMS Invincible *has four Olympus engines, the marine counterpart of the engines which power Concorde.*

Avon, of which over 1,000 units have been sold already for both electrical power generation and oil and gas pumping duties.

The highest running time of the Avon, between overhauls, is now well in excess of 40,000 hours. This has been proved with an engine used for pumping gas in the USA where the Avon is used extensively in electrical generating sets and gas-compressor and gas-pressurisation stations built by other industrial companies.

In Great Britain, Avon engines are used in large numbers by the British Gas Corporation to pump North Sea natural gas along the pipeline network in England. The engine is also being used on North Sea production platforms to pump oil and gas to the mainland. Overseas its popularity has grown steadily, and it is now a major power source in the Middle East. In addition, over fifty Avons have been delivered to pump gas in the Soviet Union.

Opposite: *The Shell Leman North Sea gas platform has a combination of Avon and RB211 engines.*

The trans-Canada pipeline at Winnipeg. Two Avons and one Spey keep the oil flowing.

Opposite: *This standby power station in New York City uses one Avon engine.*

Other Rolls-Royce engines now extensively employed in various land-based industrial roles include the Olympus, Proteus, Spey and RB211, and collectively these engines have now accumulated well over eight million running hours in operational service.

In the offshore role alone, there have been more than ninety orders for aero-derived gas-turbine engines world-wide, worth more than £60 million to the company. Seventy of these installations are in the North Sea, providing power for fourteen oil and gas fields, while the rest are in the Arabian Sea, around the Persian Gulf and in Venezualan waters.

As well as providing individual power-units, the company can supply complete power-station packages, standard gas-turbine turbo-generators, plant for offshore gas and oil platforms, and multiple power-plant sets for use in big turbine halls at power stations. The range of uses of these aero-derived power units expands every year. Already, they cover many kinds of sea-going craft. Other tasks extend from the pumping of Siberian gas and Alaskan oil to providing energy to keep North Sea oil platforms on stream; and from supplying peak power for the London Underground railway network and emergency power at Middle Eastern hospitals, to generating some twelve million kilowatts of electrical power world-wide.

The opportunities are thus immense. It has been estimated that there is likely to be a demand through the 1980s for many thousands of miles of oil and gas pipelines throughout the world. And in the developing Third World the future demand for power stations of all kinds to provide electricity for expanding domestic and industrial uses must also be enormous.

So far, its maritime uses have been largely confined to hovercraft and naval vessels, but there is clearly a massive opportunity for converting the world's commercial fleets to gas-turbine power, while the offshore oil industry will expand as demands for hydro-carbon fuels themselves increase.

Rolls-Royce is not only dedicated to meeting all these needs as they arise, but is also studying means of producing power in new ways, for the longer-term future when the world's reserves of hydro-carbon fuels diminish. The possibility of producing liquid fuels of various kinds, such as those derived from the liquefaction of coal, is being vigorously explored, with a view to developing, perhaps within the next decade or so, a commercially viable plant for their production.

13 HARNESSING NUCLEAR ENERGY

HMS Swiftsure *is a Fleet submarine, conventionally armed with torpedoes, and can be used against other submarines or surface vessels.*

In the early post-war period, it became clear that the development of nuclear energy was bound to extend beyond the military sphere, and throughout the world there was increasing interest in the development of this new source of power for a wide variety of uses.

Rolls-Royce's initial interest stemmed from the consideration that at some stage, aero-engines themselves might need to be nuclear-powered. Indeed there was considerable research into this form of aircraft propulsion in the United States. But when it became evident that this would remain a remote possibility for a long time, the company turned its attention to other requirements for nuclear power. It was clear that this was a field where the company's high quality of engineering design, and its strong technical background, could be of major significance.

Design studies and experimental work on water and liquid metal reactors for a wide range of land, sea and air applications were carried out in the 1950's, and by 1956, the company had designed and supplied its first reactor, Neptune, a low-power research facility. Rolls-Royce and Associates was formed in 1959, to handle the procurement of Britain's first submarine pressurised water reactor (PWR) for the Royal Navy, based on Anglo-US governmental agreements that initially provided for the exchange of equipment and information with the American company, Westinghouse.

Rolls-Royce's partners in this new company were Foster Wheeler and Vickers: Babcock & Wilcox became a partner later (in 1967), with Rolls-Royce retaining overall control. As a result of the work done by this company (and by its constituent members on their own account), a substantial volume of knowledge on the design and manufacture of pressurised water-cooled reactors for submarines has been acquired. This company has supplied all the PWR's for the Royal Navy's nuclear submarine programme, from the original *Dreadnought*, through the Polaris missile-carrying submarines (*Resolution,*

HMS Dreadnought, *Britain's first nuclear submarine, made a spectacular departure at speed when she left Faslane for Chatham where she was refitted in 1974. She is conventionally armed with homing torpedoes, but is capable of continuous patrols at high speed underwater, independent of base support and can circumnavigate the globe without surfacing.*

The Polaris submarine, HMS Resolution, *returning to Faslane in the Firth of Clyde.* Resolution, *which carries 16 missiles, is one of four Royal Navy Polaris submarines. Once at sea, they are lost to the enemy, with almost unlimited endurance, and can range the oceans freely with little fear of detection. One Polaris submarine has a fire power greater than all the bombs dropped by both sides during the Second World War.*

Repulse, Renown and *Revenge*), to the long line of Fleet (anti-submarine hunter-killer) nuclear submarines. In addition, since 1965 it has managed and operated the shore-based prototype reactor plant at Dounreay in Scotland on behalf of the Ministry of Defence. A specialised manufacturing facility, purpose-built by Rolls-Royce in 1961, has made all the nuclear cores for all Rolls-Royce and Associates reactor plants currently in service.

Rolls-Royce's long term interest in nuclear power goes well beyond military uses, and since the early '60s a modest-sized team has been studying other applications, in such fields as electric power generation, ship propulsion and under-sea power-plants.

Presaging the major contribution the PWR would make to nuclear electric power generation, Rolls-Royce in conjunction with English Electric, tendered for the Dungeness B project in 1964. Also, in 1968, Rolls-Royce completed a comprehensive study of a closed-cycle helium-cooled reactor using the company's gas turbines.

More recently, since 1977, Rolls-Royce has been working on a design for a standardised range of prefabricated PWR plant, intended to eliminate the delays involved in the design, safety, licensing, construction, installation and commissioning of nuclear power stations. The objective has been to provide generating capacity of high quality and reliability. For small plants, the power station could be constructed as a unit, basically comprising a PWR with associated equipment and turbines, mounted together on a floating barge or barges.

The nuclear plant, including the barge, would be built under factory conditions, using normal production-line techniques, at a shipyard, and then towed to a suitable site, floated into position, settled on to its preprepared supports and finally connected to a power-distribution system. Only a limited amount of civil engineering work would be needed at the final destination, to bring the unit ashore from the river, canal or seaside point to which it had been floated. By using this system, it will be possible to produce nuclear power stations sequentially and continually at a more economic cost than doing all the construction operations on the final sites, as is the current general practice. Moreover, by undertaking the overall manufacture of the nuclear power package under factory-controlled conditions, much greater management control would be assured, while the resultant quality of all workmanship involved will be of a higher standard.

This technique is considered most suited for

HMS Sovereign *is the Royal Navy's seventh nuclear-powered Fleet submarine. Her primary role is as a hunter-killer, and she is fitted with the latest underwater detection equipment and weapons. She has an inertial navigation system and a means of measuring her depth below the ice.*

The Polaris submarine, HMS Renown.

small, single PWR plants up to 400 megawatts output, and thus ideally located in areas where power demands do not require larger stations. Most nuclear power stations at present have outputs between 600 and 1,300 megawatts and clearly are unsuitable for such locations.

In parallel with its power station studies Rolls-Royce has developed its interest in the marine nuclear field. In 1975, with the General Electric Company of the UK it formed Ship Propulsion Limited to design and manufacture marine PWR propulsion plants, and in particular to tender for a PWR to be used in a big Canadian ice-breaker ship project. Although that venture has not materialised, Rolls-Royce has continued its studies of ice-breaker and other marine plant, in the anticipation that at some point in the future commercial marine nuclear propulsion will become a reality.

One of the most imaginative ventures recently under study by Rolls-Royce, is for an under-sea "nuclear power module", intended to supply continuous power for very deep water applications, such as drilling for oil and other minerals locked beneath the oceans at depths well beyond those where oil and gas have been found to date. This study was carried out in association with other commercial organisations such as Sir Robert McAlpine and BICC.

Fixed installations offshore, such as those used to produce oil from the North Sea, are feasible in waters up to 330 feet (200 metres) deep. For depths beyond that it becomes very expensive, as well as very difficult to provide installations with their bases resting on the sea-bed, and their working deck areas above the waves. Such structures would have to be gigantic in size, and very strong to withstand the forces of wind and water to which they would be subjected in very deep seas.

Thus, under-sea mobile drilling platforms seem a more suitable solution. They would be developed as part of a major complex of living and working facilities, located on one spot on the sea-bed perhaps for years, but then capable of being moved on elsewhere for further duties. Self-contained power supplies for such devices could most economically be provided over long periods by nuclear power-plants, of the kind the

A design for an undersea oil production facility, for oil recovery and processing at depths in excess of 500m. Power is produced by a conventional two loop pressurised water reactor. 1) gas flare; 2) reservoirs; 3) production equipment module; 4) drilling template; 5) power modules; 6) power module docking terminal; 7) living quarters; 8) storage outlet module; 9) sea-bed flowlines; 10) reservoirs; 11) mid-ocean terminal loading buoy.

company has become skilled at designing for other uses.

The Rolls-Royce under-sea nuclear power module has thus evolved as possibly a major contribution in solving the problem of obtaining hydro-carbon fuels and precious minerals from the very deep ocean floors of the world.

All these ventures indicate that Rolls-Royce, and its associated companies, have built up already a capability in the nuclear power field that covers the entire spectrum of design, development and construction of reactor plants and components. The teams concerned have evolved a considerable degree of expertise in project management and planning, together with a high reputation for ensuring safety in their projects. Although by comparison with aero-engine, industrial and marine gas turbine programmes, the company's nuclear power activity is small, it might, nonetheless, be highly significant in its implications for the longer-term future of Rolls-Royce.

14 ROLLS-ROYCE PEOPLE

Opposite: *A 40/50hp Silver Ghost taking employees' children on a picnic circa* 1907 or 1908.

As with any other great organisation, the life-blood of Rolls-Royce is its work-force, at all levels. With about 60,000 employees, Rolls-Royce is not only one of the largest individual industrial organisations in the United Kingdom, but it is also, and always has been, one of the most conscious of the need for a high level of training, and for welfare.

In its early days, the company was sufficiently small to be paternalistic in its approach to its workers – although Royce, Johnson and Hives all acquired reputations for driving their employees very hard. In the early days at Cooke Street this meant a 57-hour basic working week, often with overtime as well. The weekly wage for a skilled man would be thirty shillings a week.

There are many tales about Royce which reflect both his generosity and his unpredictability. On one occasion he lent money for the funeral to a distressed worker who would not otherwise have been able to afford a decent burial for his wife. On another occasion Royce lent his own car to an employee so that the young man and his bride could have a honeymoon. Yet he had also been known to refuse a junior manager time off for a honeymoon, because he disapproved of that marriage. Royce hated waste, and no-one at Le Canadel was allowed to throw away a pencil stub; a bit of bamboo from the garden would serve as a handle so that the last little bit could be used. But Royce's crustiness did not sour his dry humour. He used to tease De Looze, the first company secretary, who talked about preserving the quid pro quo. Royce quipped back: "You can look after the pro quos, it's the quids I'm interested in".

Royce always remained something of an unknown quantity. He might wander cheerfully round the factory one day, puffing his pipe and sometimes singing snatches of Gilbert and Sullivan. The next day he would sack half the workforce – who would then be quietly reinstated by his colleagues. By contrast Claude Johnson had the reputation of being very kind and con-

Royce
R.540

airways
中國民

siderate. At one stage in the First World War, he used to send the managers to the theatre in Derby once a week at Rolls-Royce expense to ensure that they had a break from the work and strain. He kept quiet about it though, as Royce would not have approved.

Between the wars Rolls-Royce fitters and engineers travelled extensively, often at a moment's notice. Alan Cobham's aircraft suffered an engine problem during his famous trans-Africa flight. The engineer who accompanied the replacement engine across to Africa and up a crocodile-infested river set to work immediately his fatiguing journey was over, and installed it. The reputation for excellence and service established by such feats paid dividends. Large numbers of Rolls-Royce cars were sold in some surprising places. The Maharajah of Bharatpur actually had about fifty Rolls-Royces at one time. Another maharajah, when asked if he would like one of the new 20hp models simply replied: "Oh, send me the first half dozen".

Ernest Hives used to drive his cars and his workforce fast and furiously, and it was under his direction that the Rolls-Royce effort in World War Two was so successful. After the war Rolls-Royce had an enormous capacity to produce light metal alloy castings, and new ideas were being suggested for production. They experimented with a saucepan. At the first ceremonial boiling of an egg, the pan toppled over when it was lifted, because the handle was below the centre of gravity. Hives's reaction was: "Ah well, that teaches us not to meddle with things we don't understand. Let's stick to the things we know about." It is amusing to think how close the Rolls-Royce name came to being associated with an article as simple and pragmatic as a saucepan. The incident effectively terminated any thoughts that senior executives might have had about product diversification.

Inevitably, as the company grew larger, much of the old paternalism disappeared and following the bankruptcy of 1971 when some of the older members of the work-force left the company, much of the former atmosphere of comradeship amongst long-serving members of the staff disappeared. It cannot be denied that morale took a severe hammering as a result of the bankruptcy, and it has taken much of the ensuing decade to correct that situation. Even so, Rolls-Royce still has a strong affinity with many

A group of senior Rolls-Royce officials photographed in the mid-1930's. Front row, left to right: Eric Platford, Arthur Wormald, William Cowen, Captain Hallam, and Tom Haldenby. Back row: R.W. Harvey-Bailey, Sir Arthur Sidgreaves, Ernest Hives and John De Looze.

Opposite: *The Rolls-Royce team in China. Sir Kenneth Keith and Sir Stanley Hooker (centre) with other senior officials. Dennis Head, then managing director, aero division, is on the extreme right.*

These photographs illustrate something of the wide range of modern engineering and design skills employed at Rolls-Royce and which feature in apprentice training.

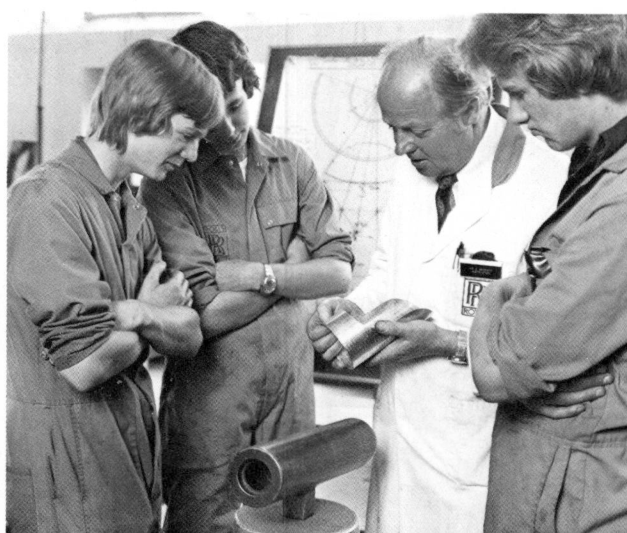

Chairman Hua of China signing the visitors' book at Rolls-Royce, Derby, in 1979

Sir Kenneth Keith photographed during his last visit to the Derby works before retiring.

of its employees, many of whom have spent their entire working lives with the company.

Indeed, one of the most significant aspects of the company today is the very large number of long-service personnel to be found on the payroll. It is not difficult to find families in Derby and its surrounding communities who have given two, and in some cases even three, generations of service to Rolls-Royce. Half of the present labour force have been with the company for at least ten years, and of those, about one-third, or some 10,000, have been with the company for more than 25 years, a most impressive statistic.

The sense of belonging to a special company is perhaps best epitomised in the habit long ago adopted of referring to senior personnel by initials, rather than by names. Thus Ernest Hives was always known as "Hs", and Sir Denning Pearson as "Psn". Throughout management at least, everyone knew who was meant. The feeling of belonging is evident at all levels. Its strength was even demonstrated on one occasion by the presence on site at a weekend of senior union representatives during an overtime ban. They were that keen to see an important project finished on schedule. Until they bumped into each other, neither man had known that the other was breaking the ban which they were both meant to be enforcing. The family feeling has surfaced in more flippant ways too over the years – amongst young apprentices who have been known for instance to drill tiny holes below the rim of the enamel tea mugs, the old men never understanding why they suddenly start to dribble.

The first company welfare schemes were proposed as early as December, 1918, when Claude Johnson suggested issuing 200,000 ordinary shares to the workers. Sports and social facilities were provided at about the same time.

Lord McFadzean (far left) who was appointed chairman of Rolls-Royce in January 1980. Left: during one of his visits to the company's factories. He is seen talking to a fitter working on Gem engines at Leavesden.

Another proposal by Johnson for workers' representatives on the board was rejected outright by his somewhat startled fellow-directors. The workers' shares scheme did not come to fruition until 1920, but it remained in existence until the bankruptcy of 1971, when there were 12,000 workers holding nearly £2m in shares. In 1959 a long service award scheme was introduced.

Rolls-Royce's most important contribution to its employees is in training and education. It offers excellent apprenticeships, and runs many other internal training programmes across a wide range of technical skills and scientific disciplines. The company also makes extensive use of external educational facilities at universities and colleges.

Engineering staff from Saudia, the Saudi Arabian airline, at Derby learning to maintain RB211 engines. Rolls-Royce runs training courses for customer staff from many countries.

15 A FUTURE FULL OF CHALLENGE

Throughout its seventy-five years, Rolls-Royce has weathered many vicissitudes, including the worst that can befall any commercial organisation: bankruptcy. That it has been able to survive and attain its present position of technological strength is a tribute largely to the many thousands of dedicated workers who in many cases have devoted their entire working lives to the company's service. There has always been an ingrained belief in management and workers, stemming back to Royce himself, that technological excellence is not only worth striving for in its own right, but can also be well rewarded in the long-term.

It could be argued that it was the pursuit of such technological excellence that brought down the former Rolls-Royce Limited in 1971, but that subsequent events have demonstrated that the decision of the early 1960s to develop the RB211 has proved justified, in that it has opened up for the company a place in world aero-engine markets that it would not otherwise have achieved. Of course, the price that has been paid has been heavy, and commercial considerations, such as the need for profitability, cannot be ignored in this search for engineering perfection. Today, the company still faces the formidable task of substantially raising its aero-engine production in a short period of time, to meet the contractual commitments it has undertaken, and thus secure its position in world markets.

It is worth considering, however, what the alternative might have been over the ensuing years of this century had the RB211 been abandoned and Rolls-Royce not been rescued in 1971. The company would no longer have been in world aero-engine markets in any meaningful way. There would have been no continuous thread of advanced technological development upon which to base many further ventures now in progress, such as the expansion of the military, industrial and marine applications.

Rolls-Royce would have either disappeared entirely, or been relegated to the status of a

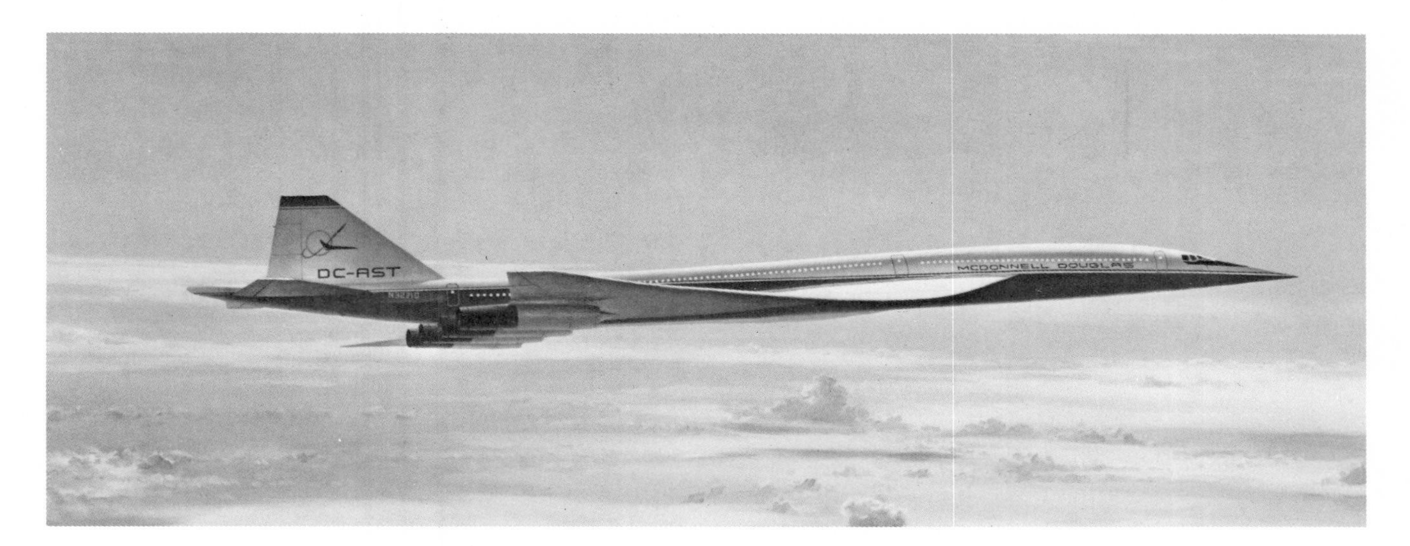

A McDonnell Douglas study for an advanced supersonic transport (AST), which could be built as a second-generation supersonic airliner to succeed Concorde.

This 250-passenger aircraft would be designed for short takeoffs and landings with lower noise levels. The jet thrust over the top of the wing would follow the curve of the wing and flaps to produce lift as well as forward thrust. It would enable passengers travelling relatively short distances of 500 miles or less to use smaller airports closer to the city.

second or even third rank aero-engine company. The UK would now be buying virtually all of its civil and military power-plants from overseas, probably mainly from the United States, with all that that implies for the country's balance of payments. It would also have lost that spearhead of technological endeavour without which no advanced industrial nation can hope to survive, let alone succeed, in a world that is increasingly technologically orientated.

The company's expertise in advanced technology was rescued when the old Rolls-Royce Limited was translated into Rolls-Royce (1971) and a measure of the most valuable continuity of engineering experience was preserved. It is upon that foundation that the company has been able to build over the past decade.

Today, the company still faces considerable financial and technological challenges as a result of the rapid changes in the political and economic conditions of the world in which it has to operate. Across the entire spectrum of engine

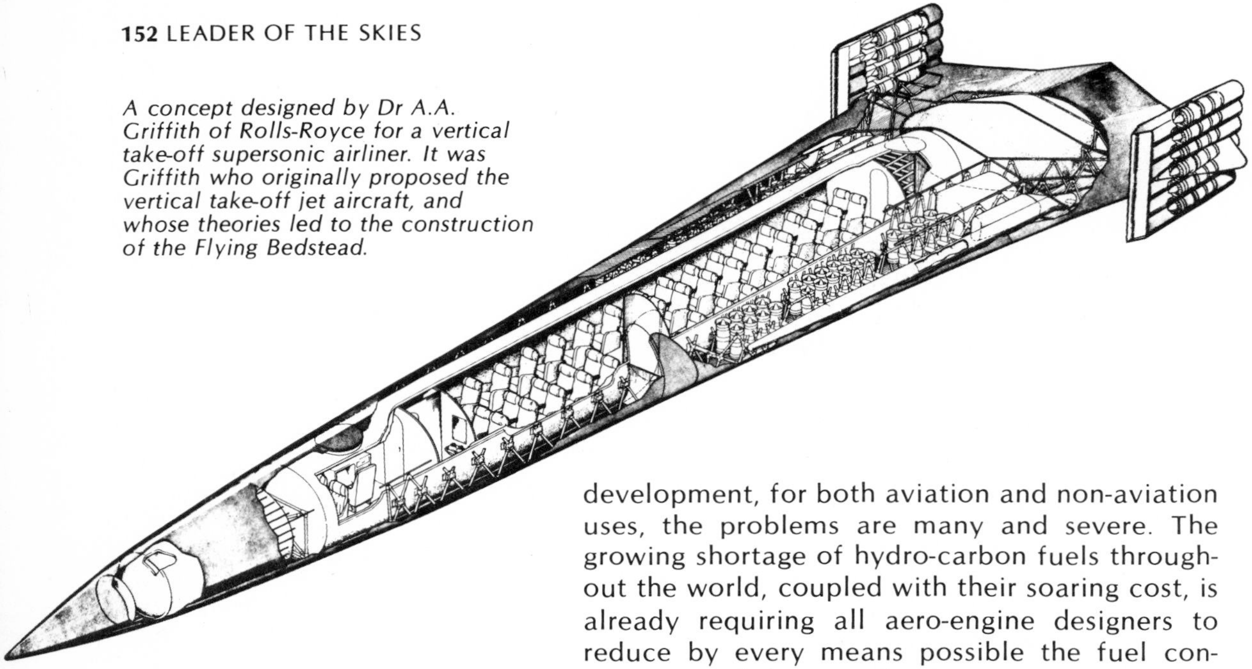

A concept designed by Dr A.A. Griffith of Rolls-Royce for a vertical take-off supersonic airliner. It was Griffith who originally proposed the vertical take-off jet aircraft, and whose theories led to the construction of the Flying Bedstead.

Opposite: *This concept of a "distributed load freighter", pictured by a Boeing Commercial Airplane Company artist, is a 12-engined giant designed to carry specialized freight such as crude oil at a much lower cost per pound than is possible today. It would operate only from airfields dedicated to air freight. Payload is taken on through the wing tip and distributed all through the wing, enabling lighter, less expensive structure. This concept is one among many that Boeing is studying as a possibility for the future.*

development, for both aviation and non-aviation uses, the problems are many and severe. The growing shortage of hydro-carbon fuels throughout the world, coupled with their soaring cost, is already requiring all aero-engine designers to reduce by every means possible the fuel consumption of their products. It is imperative not only to make every new generation of engines less fuel-thirsty than those which went before, but also to improve existing engines almost continuously, so as to ensure that their operators can survive themselves in an age increasingly sensitive to costs and prices.

This vital need to conserve fuel will probably mean propellor turbine engines remaining in service much longer than was envisaged only a few years ago. Continuing orders for the Fokker F27 Friendship and the British Aerospace 748 short-to-medium range airliners, both powered by two Rolls-Royce Dart turboprops which have been in production for some thirty years, is evidence of this.

Turboprops use less fuel than jet engines but their power output is limited because of problems which arise when the propellors are driven so fast that their tips are whirring around at the speed of sound. For several years designers have been looking at new propellors which may beat this problem and enable aircraft to fly at nearly the same speed as jet airliners.

Entirely new turboprop designs may emerge in the future. They will use some of the technology developed for jet engines in the last quarter of a century since the last big turbojet was designed. For such engines there could be an entirely fresh role – powering 100-seater airliners for the shorter routes which are now flown by the fuel-thirsty jets.

At the same time, it is essential to widen the search for techniques of using alternative fuels. The possibilities include liquid hydrogen or fuels derived from the liquefaction of coal, both of which are being considered for the longer-term future, and which will perhaps call for power units of new designs and some modification of existing types of engine.

Further, there is the increasingly significant area of environmental protection to be considered, both in terms of noise and pollution. It must be accepted that the environmental objections to civil aviation over the past twenty years have increased in strength, not without some justification, imposing new disciplines upon aero-engine designers to ensure that their products are and will remain socially acceptable to the community at large. This search for quieter and cleaner power-plants, which at the same time must be more economical to buy and fly, is not only sociologically and economically necessary, but also fundamentally desirable and even inevitable. It is the purpose of technology ultimately to serve mankind, in whatever field of endeavour, and not to become its master.

Rolls-Royce fully recognises this requirement, and accepts all the challenges willingly. It is already devoting a substantial proportion of its

BOEING

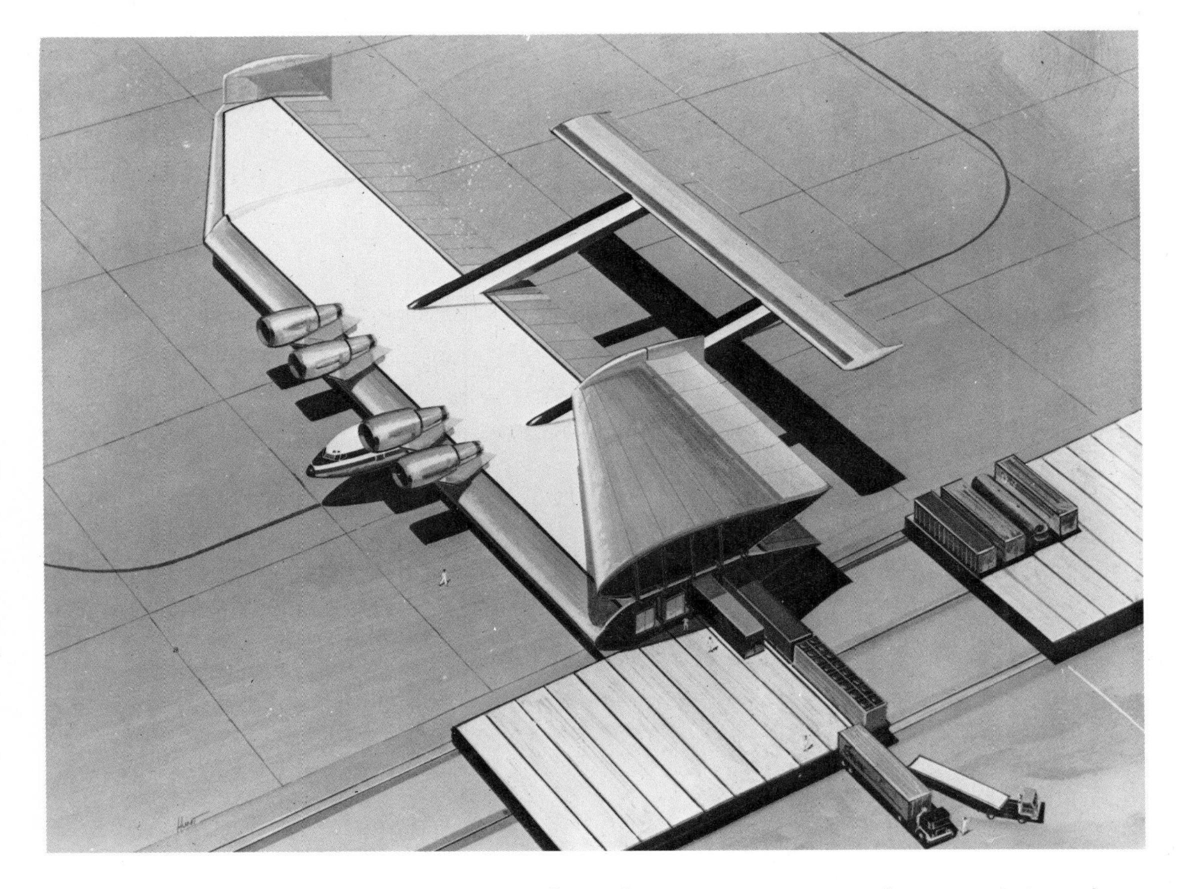

One of the Boeing preliminary design staff's "distributed load freighter" concepts is shown loading truck-sized containers through a wing tip. These containers are packed down the entire length of the giant wing enabling lighter and less expensive structure and better operating costs than are possible today. This concept is one among many that Boeing is studying as a possibility for the future.

technical resources not only to solving these current problems, but also to looking ahead to ascertain what new problems may emerge in the twenty-first century and to find ways of meeting them.

In addition to these technical and social challenges, there are the purely commercial obstacles to surmount. Competition in world aerospace as a whole is becoming fiercer every year. The world economic situation itself is now much less stable than it was a few years ago, with high inflation and recession in some countries. Although this may be a passing phase, it nonetheless creates tougher business conditions which the company must accept and surmount.

It is probable, too, that as the cost and complexity of modern civil and military aero-engines continue to rise, the necessity for international collaboration will increase. Indeed, it already seems likely that no new civil or military aero-engine, other than the very smallest, will ever again be developed solely by any one company in any one country, and it is significant that even the mighty United States companies are making greater use of international collaboration in their new-generation airframes and engines, as Rolls-Royce itself has done for many years.

Against all these problems, however, one basic fact can be set – that aviation as a tool of mankind is likely to continue to grow in both volume and importance. Although there may be periods of economic boom and slump, inexorably the number of people who will fly throughout the world will increase every year. Ever since passenger air travel became a reality, just after the First World War, the numbers using it have grown.

In 1980, for example, it is estimated that well over 800 million people flew on scheduled air services throughout the world, and this figure is probably raised to well over the 1,000 millions mark if the non-scheduled and charter passengers are also included.

Even this figure, however, is but a fraction of the total population of the world. Many millions of people even in the industrially-developed and air transport-saturated regions of the world – particularly North America, Western Europe, and Japan – still have never taken to the air. It must also be remembered that many of those who do fly become airborne on more than one occasion during the year, so that the actual number of individuals who have travelled by air is much less than 1,000 million per year. Thus, it can be seen that passenger aviation still has a long way to go before it reaches saturation point in its development.

The carriage of cargo, too, still has a boundless future in front of it. So far, the concept of aerial distribution of goods has been accepted by comparatively few industrialists even in the highly developed nations, and the era of the giant cargo jets has yet to arrive - although the all-cargo Jumbos have made a significant breakthrough in this respect. But the day of "resource transports", carrying bulk cargoes of oil or grain by air, has yet to come, and when it does, it promises to revolutionise industrial and even economic concepts in many countries.

However, man as yet has barely begun to explore all the possible uses he can make of aviation. The era of the small, truly "bus-stop" jet airliner is not with us yet, but it may arrive. There are myriad new uses emerging for the ubiquitous helicopter. The massive Boeing 747 Jumbo jets are already being enlarged, and the day of the "thousand-seater" airliner is on the way.

It is also possible that in future, new concepts will emerge that will make journeys from one side of the world to the other as commonplace as short-haul air travel is today. Supersonic airliners like Concorde have already halved journey times on routes to New York, Washington and Singapore from Europe, and a second-generation advanced supersonic transport is already regarded as inevitable by many airframe and engine designers. Astronauts already circle the globe in their capsules in little more than ninety minutes, and it can only be a matter of time before even the newest of the space travel devices, the American space shuttle, due for launching this year, is adopted for passenger roles.

The commercial prospects for civil aviation are thus excellent in the long-term. In military aviation, despite the natural desire for disarmament in many countries, the realities of life in the modern world are such that military aircraft and engines will continue to be in demand in substantial numbers for as far ahead as anyone can now foresee.

These are only some of the elements of a

Lockheed-Georgia Company's engineers have designed this "Flatbed" type of heavy cargo-lifter for the future, which could carry a wide variety of payloads, including if desired a separate passenger cabin, for long distance routes. Such an aircraft could be powered by Rolls-Royce high-thrust civil turbo-fan engines.

One of Lockheed-Georgia Company's futuristic aircraft designs, with three separate fuselage sections and a gross weight of 1.5 million pounds (680,000kg). Such an aircraft could be powered by Rolls-Royce engines.

Lockheed Georgia Company's engineers have designed this "Flatbed" type of heavy cargo-lifter for the future, which could carry a wide variety of payloads, including if desired a separate passenger cabin, for long distance routes. Such an aircraft could be powered by Rolls-Royce high-thrust civil turbo-fan engines.

future that is full of challenge. Collectively, they will create a demand for aeronautical vehicles of all kinds, and for the engines to power them, which Rolls-Royce is already, and intends to continue to be, in a position to provide.

The most significant justification of all for the continued existence of a company such as Rolls-Royce lies in the fundamental concept of any modern industrial society – the need not only to survive but also to ensure a good standard of life for its people.

Britain itself is an island, with inexpandable frontiers, and with a population that, even if it remains stable in numbers, will still rightly demand a rising standard of living. Apart from its temperate climate, which makes it a great agricultural nation of the world, and its reserves of North Sea oil and gas, and coal, this island has few natural resources. It can therefore only survive by using the quality of its people, by using

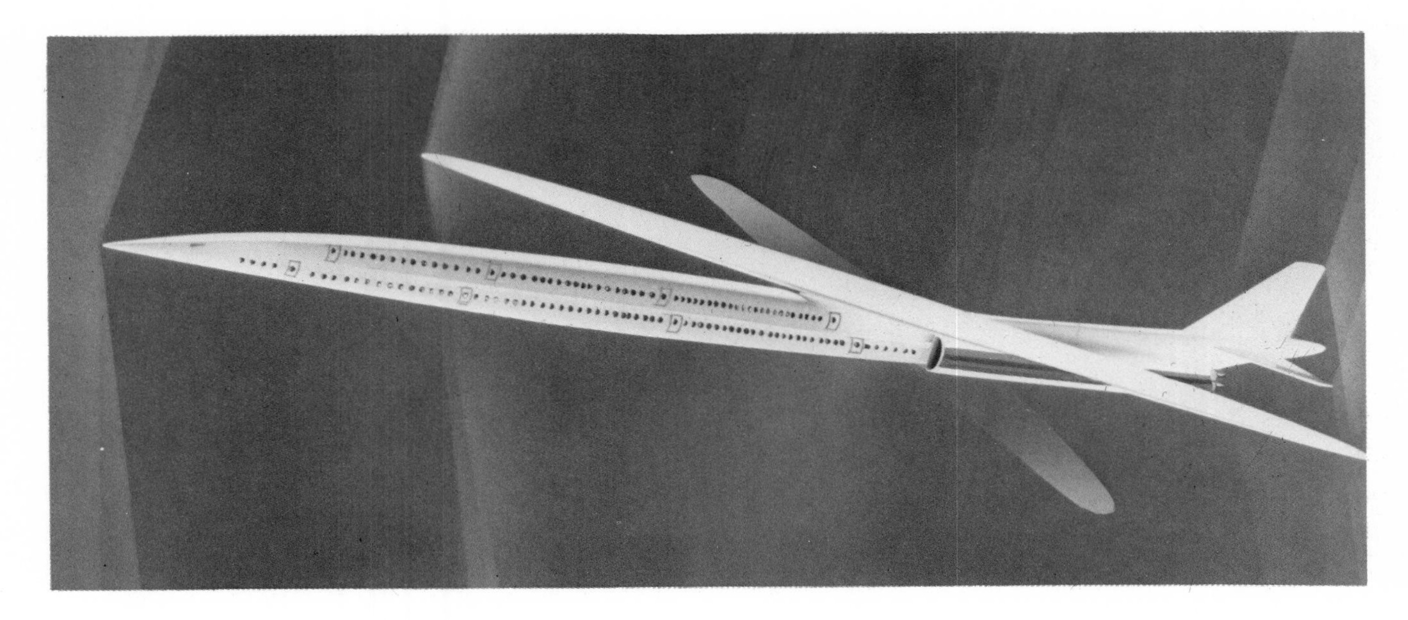

This oblique wing or "yawed wing" design would fly slightly faster than the speed of sound with the wing pivoted forward but could land and take off as slowly as today's jets with the wing pivoted perpendicular to the fuselage, or straight across. The unusual design promises to reduce drag. Rolls-Royce engines could produce lower noise levels. Such an aircraft would be easier to build than current supersonic transport designs, although it would not be designed to fly as fast as Concorde.

A design for a large sea loiter aircraft by Lockheed. It could take a huge payload of weapons, fly 3,200 nautical miles (5,926km), and land on the sea in a force 5 wind. Take off and landing would be assisted by a hydroski. Such an aircraft could use Rolls-Royce military engines.

the skills of their brains and hands to convert imported raw materials at economic cost into products which the rest of the world will buy.

For an island trading nation such as Britain in an increasingly complex and competitive industrial era, there is no alternative to the existence of highly-motivated, technologically-orientated companies such as Rolls-Royce, reared in the concept and dedicated to the furtherance of engineering excellence. Without such organisations, the economic and social future of this nation would be bleak indeed.

Rolls-Royce has survived seventy-five turbulent sometimes traumatic years. The next seventy-five may be no less turbulent. But it is already clear that there will be no lack of ability or will with which to meet the challenges that lie in the decades ahead, and abundant rewards await the company if it can successfully meet them.

BIBLIOGRAPHY

The bibliography given below represents only a proportion of the many sources consulted – books, newspapers, magazines, historical documents, etc. The books included herein, however, constitute a reasonably comprehensive list of follow-up reading for those interested in aeronautical history over the past seventy-five years, and the history of Rolls-Royce in particular.

Allen, John E. and Bruce, Joan (eds.). *The Future of Aeronautics.* Hutchinson, London, 1970.
Banks, Air Commodore F.R. *I Kept No Diary.* Airlife Publications, Shrewsbury, 1978.
Barker, Ralph. *The Schneider Trophy Races.* Chatto & Windus, London, 1971.
Barnes, C.H. *Shorts Aircraft Since 1900.* Putnam, London, 1967.
Brabazon of Tara, Lord. *The Brabazon Story.* Heinemann, London, 1956.
Dean, Sir Maurice. *The Royal Air Force* and *Two World Wars.* Cassell, London, 1979.
Department of Trade. *Report Into the Financial Affairs of Rolls-Royce.* HMSO, London, 1973.
Eves, Edward. *Rolls-Royce, 75 Years of Motoring Excellence.* Orbis Publishing, London, 1980.
Gibbs-Smith, C.H. *The Aeroplane: An Historical Survey.* Science Museum (HMSO), London, 1960 (and revised and expanded edition, 1970).
Gibbs-Smith, C.H. *Sir George Cayley's Aeronautics, 1796-1855 A Science Museum Handbook* (HMSO), London, 1962.
Gibbs-Smith, C.H. *The Rebirth of European Aviation.* Science Museum, HMSO, London, 1974.
Harker, R.W. *Rolls-Royce From The Wings 1925-1971.* Oxford Illustrated Press, 1976.
Harker, R.W. *The Engines Were Rolls-Royce.* Macmillan Publishing, New York, 1980.
Henshaw, Alex. *Sigh For A Merlin (Testing The Spitfire)* John Murray, London, 1979.
Jackson, A.J. *Blackburn Aircraft Since 1909.* Putnam, London, 1968.
James, Derek N. *Gloster Aircraft Since 1917.* Putnam, London, 1971.
Jane's All The World's Aircraft. (Appears annually.) Macdonald & Co.
Jane's Historical Aircraft, 1902-1916. (A facsimile reprint from *Jane's All The World's Aircraft, 1917*); Macdonald & Co., London, 1972.
Keith, Sir Kenneth (*et al*). *The Achievement of Excellence, the Story of Rolls-Royce.* (A paper for the Newcomen Society in the USA) 28th October, 1976.
Lewis, Peter. *The British Bomber Since 1914.* Putnam, London, 1967.
Lloyd, Ian. *Rolls-Royce, The Growth of a Firm.* Macmillan Press, London, 1978.
Lloyd, Ian. *Rolls-Royce, The Years of Endeavour.* Macmillan Press, London, 1978.
Lloyd, Ian. *Rolls-Royce, The Merlin At War.* Macmillan Press, London, 1978.
Pearson, Sir Denning. *The Development and Organisation of Rolls-Royce Limited.* (a paper for the London School of Economics and Political Science) November, 1964.
Pemberton, Sir Max. *The Life of Sir Henry Royce.* Selwyn & Blount, London.
Penrose, Harald. *British Aviation, The Pioneer Years, 1903-1914.* Putnam, London, 1967.
Penrose, Harald. *British Aviation, The Great War & Armistice, 1915-1919.* Putnam, London, 1969.
Penrose, Harald. *British Aviation, The Adventuring Years, 1920-29.* Putnam, London, 1973.
Penrose, Harald. *British Aviation, Widening Horizons, 1930-1934.* Royal Air Force Museum (HMSO), London, 1979.
Penrose, Harald. *Wings Across The World, A Pictorial History of British Airways.* Cassell, London, 1980.
Reed, Arthur. *Britain's Aircraft Industry (What Went Right, What Went Wrong).* M. Dent, London, 1973.
Rolls-Royce Limited. *A Brief History of The Birth and Development of The Merlin Aero-Engine.* November, 1945. Rolls-Royce Limited and Rolls-Royce (1971). Various annual reports.
Rolls-Royce Limited. *Engine Status Report, 1980.* (prepared for the Farnborough International Air Show).
Rolls-Royce Limited. *The Rolls-Royce Magazine,* all issues.
Rolls-Royce Limited. *Rolls-Royce News,* all issues.
Solberg, Carl. *The Conquest of the Skies (A History of Commercial Aviation in America).* Little, Brown & Company, Boston, 1979.
Stinton, Darrol. *The Anatomy of the Aeroplane.* G.T. Foulis, London, 1966.
Taylor, John W.R. and Munson, Kenneth (eds.). *History of Aviation.* New English Library, London, 1972.
Taylor, John W.R. *The Lore of Flight,* Thomas Nelson & Sons, London, 1973.
Thetford, Owen. *Aircraft of the Royal Air Force Since 1918.* Putnam, London, 1957.
Turner, P. St. John. *The Vickers Vimy.* Patrick Stephens, London, 1969.
Walker, Percy B. *Early Aviation at Farnborough.* Macdonald & Company, London, 1971.
Wallace, Graham. *The Flight of Alcock and Brown, June 14-15, 1919.* Putnam, London, 1955.
Walsh, John Evangelist. *First Flight, The Untold Story of the Wright Brothers.* George Allen & Unwin, London, 1976.
Wood, Derek. *Project Cancelled.* Macdonald & Jane's, London, 1975.
Wood, Derek & Derek Dempster. *The Narrow Margin, The Battle of Britain and the Rise of Air Power.* Hutchinson, London, 1961.

INDEX

Numbers in *italic type* refer to illustrations.